The Bell IN THE Tree

Thirty stories from Glasgow's past

Edward H. Chisnall

COLLINS
in association with

RADIO CLYDE 261

First published 1983, reprinted 1984

Copyright © Edward H. Chisnall and Radio Clyde 1983

ISBN 0 00 435687 10
Typeset by C. R. Barber and Partners (Highlands) Ltd.
Printed by Collins, Glasgow

This book is dedicated
TO MARGARET

The Radio Clyde series
The Bell in the Tree: the Clyde Story
in 260 episodes

CAST

Gerry Slevin	*Martin Black*
Robert Trotter	*Tony Roper*
John Young	*William Armour*
Tam Dean Burn	*Roy Hanlon*
David Peate	*Phil McCall*
John Shedden	*Sharon Erskine*
Michael Elder	*Finlay Welsh*
Mary Riggans	*Paul Young*
Gwynneth Guthrie	*June Andrews*
Eileen McCallum	*Monica Gibb*
Michael McEvitt	*Jenny Angus*
James Copeland	*Finlay McLean*
Jackie Farrell	*Mike MacKenzie*
Willy Joss	*Alec Montieth*
Bill Riddoch	
Charles Kearney	WRITTEN BY
Sheila Donald	*Edward H. Chisnall*
June Kennedy	
Sandy West	PRODUCED BY
Jean Faulds	*Hamish Wilson*
Sandy Morton	

FOREWORD

The year 1983 was a special one in Glasgow. It was the year of 'Welcome Home – Pride of the Clyde', and as part of this year-long celebration of our great city, Radio Clyde created 'The Bell in the Tree'. Three times a day for a year, starting with St. Mungo, we have brought the drama and humour of the story of Glasgow and the Clyde to hundreds of thousands of our listeners.

Many, many of our listeners have written to us about the series. Here is just one of those letters:

'The telling of our story was part of this very special year in Glasgow. That our own local radio station did it, and did it so well, is a tribute to what we have come to expect from Radio Clyde.

An immense amount of interest in the history of the city was generated, not least because of the entertaining way in which the traditionally cold pages recording the past were brought to life by some of the best actors in Scotland . . .

I hope that you enjoy reading about those Glaswegians who came before us, and their effect on what life means today in so many places around the world. Every one of them helped to ensure that Glasgow's Miles Better. They were special people. Like Glaswegians are today.

The Rt Hon The Lord Provost Michael Kelly
CBE OStJ BSc (Econ) PhD'

'This very special year in Glasgow' – a year when Glasgow opened its arms to the world, a year of centenaries and bi-centenaries: the Boys' Brigade, the Royal Hospital for Sick Children, the oldest Chamber of Commerce in Britain, the oldest English-language daily newspaper, the building of the City Chambers. And, at Hogmanay, Radio Clyde will be ten years old!

What better way to celebrate our pride in the city than to tell its story through the ages?

Eddie Chisnall, who scripted the series, unearthed a wealth of fascinating details from our history, and created a host of vivid characters to bring that history to life. There was the Italian who escaped 'doon the watter' during the Glasgow Fair of 1192, the Provost of Glasgow who died on Flodden Field, the two stolid Paisleymen heaving faggots for the witch-burnings of 1677, the lad who helped James Watt build a better steam engine, the wee boy saved by Lister's antiseptic surgery, the family who found themselves planted in one of the postwar schemes – and so many more.

As the series became compulsive listening over West Central Scotland, we began to appreciate that there should be a book. The schools and libraries, the taxi drivers and policemen, the patients in hospital, the housewives and shopkeepers, the councillors and all kinds of clubs and associations, all wrote and telephoned us, asking for a book.

So here it is. What's in your hands represents some of Eddie Chisnall's wonderful story-telling. He turned his own scripts into these tales.

I would like, on your behalf, to thank Hamish Wilson, Clyde's drama producer, who worked with some of the most talented actors in Scotland to bring you 'The Bell in the Tree' on air. Eddie Chisnall deserves a medal for the job he did, but most of all thanks to every one of you who tuned in for the series – you are 'The Pride of the Clyde'.

Alex. Dickson
Programme Controller
Radio Clyde

CONTENTS

A GREY HUNTSMAN IN A GREEN PLACE

It was the year 543 A.D. The shadows of a long Dark Age had descended over Scotland, and in the kingdoms of every petty warlord-for-a-day, the swish of the sword was heard in croft and monastery, valley and forest, and men walked warily and armed, or not at all.

As the ice was breaking on the shallow river and the fresh green of spring spread slowly among the matted twigs and tangled branches, the hush of the great forest was broken by sudden cries of anguish.

'Master . . .!' cried the little man. 'Master! I'm caught!'

Stooping towards his servant struggling on the ground among last autumn's leaves, the dark-haired man freed the edge of the cloak that had caught on a sharp thorn. 'Be at peace, will you, Broag?' he smiled. 'There's nothing to fear. It's a fine morning, and we've brought the Gospel with us.'

Broag looked past his master and eyed the wall of trees ahead doubtfully. 'We haven't seen a living soul for days,' he answered, fiddling nervously with the torn edge of his cloak. 'We were telt by His Grace the Holy Servanus that this was the kingdom of . . .'

'Aye, aye,' his master interrupted him. 'Strathclyde. Strathclyde,' he repeated thoughtfully as he walked to the river bank and stood looking across the noisy waters of the shallow stream. 'Now how would this burn be called, my friend?' he asked with a twinkle in his eye.

'The Clyd or Clyde, or somesuch,' answered Broag, joining his master on the grassy bank.

'Indeed it is,' his companion answered. 'Strathclyde's river.'

'It's no' sae big,' Broag muttered, glancing over his shoulder nervously.

'No. That's true,' his master answered. 'It's no Jordan.

But somewhere, somewhere it joins the sea . . .'

As his dark-haired companion gazed across the water and down the valley, mottled with the red of the old autumn turning brown and the fresh new green lying like puffs of smoke on the hillside, Broag looked at the stream and saw down onto the sandy bed where the shadows of insects darted across the stones and clean-washed mica glittered like silver. 'Quite nice here though,' he said, and his master turned and looked at him, and smiled.

'And which way to go now?' the tall man asked himself quietly. 'This Clyde seems to say, "Further yet", but it's such a green place. I think . . . I think a little further yet, Broag my friend.'

'Whatever you think's best, Master Moncu,' agreed Broag unenthusiastically.

Moncu began to walk towards the dense forest, but realized his servant wasn't following. 'Come on Broag,' he urged. 'We must go further yet.'

'B . . . but master,' stammered Broag in a hoarse whisper. 'What . . . What about . . . THEM!'

Silent as growing grass, a company of warriors had gathered a little way off while Moncu and Broag had been standing by the rushing waters of the Clyde. The watchers stood under the shadows of the great trees, still as carved stones. They were naked except for cloth kilts dyed rough russet red or deep green. Each one carried an oval wooden shield as tall as himself and covered in stretched hide, and pointing towards the travellers, like thorns on stone bushes, gleamed a thicket of lovingly sharpened bronze swords held with the ease and strength of those accustomed to using them.

Moncu strode boldly towards them, his hands out-stretched palms upward, but the warriors' leader, a giant, bearded man, crossed the glade quickly to block his path.

'Hold, shaven-headed strangers!' this figure cried, and at his signal, the rest of his men ringed the two travellers with a circle of wicked-looking swords. 'Who are you, and what are you?' If hounds could talk to the fox before a kill, they would use the same mocking, disdainful tone as this wild-looking warrior who stood in Moncu's path, the spirals and oghams of his war-paint glistening on his forehead and bulging muscles as he spoke.

Moncu stood quite still and looked at each one of his tormentors in turn. The points of their swords dropped slightly.

'We'll have no priestly magic!' roared the bull-man, glaring at the two unarmed strangers.

'Cernunnos, the Horned God of the Woods, protects us,' he added striking the back of his left hand with his index finger to ward off the evil-eye.

'And the One God protects us,' answered Moncu quietly.

Sunlight danced on the ground between them, and in the silence that followed the watchers saw, as if for the first time, that the two men were of nearly equal height. The bearded warrior was the first to drop his gaze, but he quickly mastered himself and, striding forward, took hold of Moncu's wrist roughly. 'Bind them!' he cried, and as his men hesitated, he twisted Moncu's arm savagely, but the traveller shifted his position and stared at him calmly.

'They are only men,' roared his antagonist in fury, 'and thin as sparrows.' With his free hand he reached over and took hold of the quaking Broag by the collar. 'Master and servant,' he sneered. 'And what is your name, eh?' He avoided the dark-haired man's gaze carefully as he spoke.

'We,' answered Moncu slowly, 'are friends. I am he that the Holy Servanus calls his dear friend, his Moncu. I am Cunotegerus, and I bring news for your King. I will . . .'

'Aye, well, I "will" also, Kentigernus,' interrupted his captor. 'I will that you and that sniveller are brought before my Lord Morken the King whether you "will" or no, and you can tell him your stories . . . if you dare. So says Fergus, friend of Morken.'

'That's my wish also, Fergus,' smiled Moncu.

'Get on! Move!' roared Fergus, enraged that his prisoner seemed no more in awe of him than of a bird in the trees or a salmon in the river. 'Speak no words to them,' he shouted to his men, striding ahead. The magicians will trap you

3

with words, if you let them.'

'Don't be afraid,' Moncu whispered to Broag as they stumbled through the woods, surrounded by their captors. 'Our words are stronger than theirs.'

'I know master,' answered Broag weakly, 'but do you know where they are taking us?'

'Where I meant us to go, though it's no doing of mine,' answered his master. 'This is the place, Broag. I know it now. My Church, my Glas, will be up there on that hill. That's where I'll build . . .' A rough blow on the side of his head made him stagger as he walked.

'Silence, I said,' roared the red-bearded warrior. 'Keep your tales for my Lord the King . . . dear friend.'

As they climbed up the wooded slope in silence the trees thinned and Moncu saw clearly, rising above the Clyde, the crags he had glimpsed before. 'Yes,' he said to himself, nodding as he walked. 'Yes.'

The King did listen to him for a while, and Moncu built his little wooden church on the high ground overlooking the Clyde, beside a stream called the Molendinar. For a while a new peace descended on the valley, but then a bloody civil war cut its way across the Kingdom of Strathclyde like a scarlet sickle, and the cries of dying men mingled with shouts of triumph in the burning barley fields and the forested glens. The evil King Morken, whose pagan violence had driven Moncu into hiding, was himself murdered savagely, and the new king, Rydderich, welcomed the Bishop back to the Clyde valley from his exile among the russet hills and rocky places, and his people who had come to know and love their friend Kentigern, their Moncu . . .

Moncu stood at the door of his church. 'This planking will have to become stone before long, Broag,' he said. 'It's not so easy to set fire to. Oh, and another thing . . .'

'A moment please, Bishop,' answered Broag, his tongue sticking out of the corner of his mouth as he wrote furiously on his wax tablet. 'Wood to stone,' he muttered. '. . . ecclesia in lapis . . . or saxum maybe.'

'If your Latin's not up to it, use Cymbric, Broag,'

laughed the Bishop. 'We must keep up with the times, you know. Sacred writings in Latin of course, but the language of the people will do us well enough for day-to-day matters. Put "glas" instead of "ecclesia", then we'll all know what we are talking about.'

'Yes, Bishop,' said Broag, rubbing out what he had written with the blunt end of his stylus. 'Glas,' he wrote firmly.

Moncu looked down the slope towards the Clyde, glittering in the afternoon sunlight. A party of merchants, having made their way over the badlands to the south, were fording the shallow stream, their laden mules picking their way carefully across the shallows. To the left stood a mill and the cluster of small cottages that had grown up in the years since Rydderich had become king and the church had been rebuilt.

'Do you remember when we first came here?' Moncu asked his friend who was still writing earnestly, small parings of wax showering around him like snow in summer.

'Indeed I do,' answered Broag without looking up. 'That great hairy monster should have come to a bad end,' he added.

'He did,' answered Moncu sadly. 'Though neither of us wished it. Did we Broag?'

'Er, no Bishop, no of course not,' Broag replied, suddenly discovering a particularly troublesome spelling mistake.

'Well,' sighed Moncu, 'and now we have our Church and, it seems, the beginnings of a town, and the people come to worship, and bring their troubles too, as they should.' He smiled and shook his head. 'You know, they don't call me "Bishop" or even "Kentigern" any more. They call me "Cu" like old Servanus used to. They say this is "Cu's" Church.'

'But will I put "glas" for "church"?' said Broag, finally getting his spelling right.

'Aye, indeed,' smiled Moncu. 'Write "glas" if you wish, or even "Glascu",' and as the smoke drifted up into the still evening air, Broag went indoors for another wax tablet.

5

THE FERR HOLIDAY AND THE TALKING SWAN

In the twelfth century Glasgow was an island in a wilderness of trees. The new borough, armed with a charter from King William the Lion, held 'ane merket fair weekly' near the Greyfriars Monastery. People came and went in the wide lands round about with goods and news, and sometimes there came showpeople with strange costumes and stranger manners, with flutes and tricks and talk of faraway places.

Thomas the Fleming hoisted his leather pack more squarely on his shoulders and trudged up the hill towards the Glasgow Fair. The warm July sunshine made him sweat in the thick jerkin he had worn for the dangerous sea-journey round the coast from the south. He looked enviously at the women, ankle-deep in the cool stream that flowed down from the Cathedral as they trampled their linen, laughing and singing snatches of song.

Thomas was a well-travelled man, and he could see that this was a town that was growing, and growing quickly. All around him there was bustle and clatter and energy and the sense of urgency only to be met with in a settlement on the edge of the wild. Masons cursed sweating apprentices as they struggled to dress or manhandle blocks of sandstone into place; smoke from a blacksmith's spiralled upwards near a store of fresh-cut timber; and laden oxcarts rumbled up the rutted slope past him on their way to the Bishop's castle. He nodded to himself approvingly, and thought of the rich Flemish cloth in his pack. There were good pickings to be had here. Many backs to be clothed!

Not far from the castle there ran the shallow waters of the Girthburn and beyond it hunted criminals could find sanctuary from justice, but there were no fugitives today, only the fugitive silver and rarer gold coins of the crowd, ringing on board or box or chest as the age-old system of barter gave way to the newer invention of money.

As he wound his way among the crowds he found himself on the edge of a large noisy group of men and women who were alternately laughing and jeering at something going on just out of his view. Craning his neck to see, he was pushed violently sideways by a fat, red-faced townsman trying to make his way in the opposite direction, leaving a trail of sore feet and wounded egos as he went.

'Here, you! Who are you shovin'?' a voice bellowed in Thomas' ear aggressively.

He turned slightly and saw a lean, sallow-faced man glaring at him angrily. 'I'm sorry,' he said soothingly. 'I did not see you, my friend.'

At the sound of his Flemish accent the attitude of the sly-looking man changed dramatically. 'Oh!' he grinned toothlessly. 'Stranger ur ye? Welcome to Glasgow. Here for the fair?'

'Yes, for the fair,' said Thomas.

'Well, you've come to the right place,' the man laughed. 'What are ye sellin'?' he went on.

'Fine cloth,' answered Thomas. 'Flemish weave.'

'Oh, I'm no' in the merket myself, ye understand,' the man said hastily. 'Just askin'.'

'I'm sorry to have jostled you,' said Thomas, adjusting his pack and walking away.

'Hold on, will ye?' cried the man, running after him. 'Come and hae a look at this show.'

'No, thank you, I have no time today,' smiled Thomas. 'I must earn my bread and meat.'

'Och, ye've got all day for that,' wheedled the man. 'Samuel the Fisherman,' he added, grasping hold of Thomas' hand and pumping it up and down energetically. 'That's me. What's your name?'

'Thomas . . . Thomas Gheel.'

'Funny name that,' said Samuel. 'Gheel? What kind of name's that meant to be?'

'It's my name,' Thomas replied, offended.

'Oh well,' grinned Samuel. 'You canna help it, I suppose. Come on, you've got to see this!'

'Oh?' said Thomas with a sigh. 'What is it?'

'There you are,' grinned the sallow Samuel, realizing he had scored a victory over the merchant's indecision. 'You'll enjoy this, so you will. It's a man and a talking swan, meant to be anyway,' and he winked so alarmingly that one side of his face crumpled up like a bag drawn tight by a string.

A man stood on top of a box covered with a blue cloth. He was small and clean-shaven, but dressed in a jerkin and hose of a bewildering variety of colours. Patches of twenty different cloths were sewn together; diamonds, stars, circles and crescent moons twirled and twisted their way across his chest and down his legs, twinkling and sparkling like a carnival of constellations. On his head was perched the most outrageous hat Thomas had ever seen. Beside him, staring into the distance with an air of aristocratic boredom and an occasional half-hearted 'honk', sat a melancholy goose.

'What aboot that then?' said Samuel with a triumphant wave of his hand. 'Now, would you say that was a talking swan?'

'It looks rather like a goose to me,' answered Thomas.

'There ye are!' Samuel shouted to the crowd. 'My friend here's been all over the world, and he says that's a goose, no' a swan at all.'

The crowd roared threateningly at the multi-coloured figure on the box.

'But you are wrong,' he answered bravely. 'I, Jacopo, say this.'

'Jacopo whit?' heckled a voice from the back of the crowd. 'My dug can speak better than that goose.'

The crowd jeered the showman noisily, but the goose looked through them as if they were made of glass.

'This goose is a swan,' Jacopo continued defiantly. 'And if you do but listen, she will speak to you.'

Unable to contain himself any longer, Samuel strode forward. 'Are you saying there's something wrang with my ears?' he asked.

An expectant hush fell on the crowd.

'No, no,' said Jacopo. 'Only that you must give good attention . . .'

Before he could finish what he was saying, Samuel had pulled the little man off his perch and the two were rolling on the grass. The goose had a firm grip of Samuel's ear, and the sea of excited faces surged closer and closer to the battle when, suddenly, like a ship in full sail cleaving its way through a storm, a burly figure strode into the mob, pushing and scattering people as he went.

'Come away now!' he roared. 'Who dares disturb the Bishop's peace at the Glasgow Merket Fair?'

'It's Jimmy the Reve,' someone shouted, and suddenly the milling throng melted away like a pat of butter in a pan of hot lentils.

The reve reached down with enormous hands and set the two struggling figures on their feet in front of him. The goose reluctantly let go of Samuel's ear and retired to the background, where it sat staring at the town bailiff balefully.

'Now what's all this about?' enquired the reve, frowning at the two handfuls of men he held in front of him.

'He started it, honest,' stammered Samuel. 'He started the fight.'

'Fight?' asked Jimmy the Reve with a smile. 'What fight? I saw no "fight". I saw two rabbits struggling together on the ground, and one of them was you, Samuel of Perdyc, fisherman, or whatever you call yourself, but . . . what's this? A Spanish warship?' He glowered at Jacopo.

'No, I am an honest showman, your honour,' replied his prisoner.

'Naw, he's no',' interrupted Samuel. 'He was tellin' us that that goose there is a talking swan.'

'Even if she were a goose,' said Jacopo, 'did not geese, like watchdogs, save the ancient Romans from the Goths?'

Jimmy the Reve narrowed his eyes and looked at the showman thoughtfully. 'Are you a scholar or something?' he asked. 'Where's your hame?'

'I am from Firenze in Tuscany . . . Italia,' he added.

'Italian, eh?' said the reve. 'We don't get many Italians in Glasgow. Now! Listen ... both! Raan Corbett, Grand Master of the Knights Templar is at meat with my Lord the Bishop the day, and any more disturbance at the Fair and I'll see you both shortened an ell. Understand? And if you cause any more trouble, Jack Popo ...'

Thomas, who had been standing quietly watching the wheels of local justice grinding, decided to take a hand. He strode forward. 'My pardon, Bailiff,' he said, 'but this man Samuel was the one to start the trouble.'

The reve stifled Samuel's protests with a glance and turned to the newcomer. 'Oh?' he said. 'And who might you be when you're at hame?'

'An honest trader, sir, from Flanders.'

'Aye well, honest trader, I suggest you choose your friends with care in future. Are you still here?' he roared at Samuel. 'Get you gone to Perdyc while you still can!'

With a scowl at Thomas and Jacopo, Jimmy the Reve strode off, calling out as he went, 'Come now, buy yer wonderment at the Glasgow Merket Fair. Land by roup by Odardus, loving son of Richard Hangpudding ...'

'Thank you sir,' smiled Jacopo.

'What for?' answered Thomas. 'I know what it is like to be in a foreign land. Where are you bound for now?'

'Somewhere else,' Jacopo shrugged his shoulders. 'Classinda and I.'

'Classinda?' enquired Thomas.

'My goose,' laughed Jacopo. 'She is a good bird.'

Classinda honked her agreement.

'Well if I can give you some advice,' said Thomas. 'There is a ship leaving for Flanders soon that will give you passage.'

'Thank you,' said Jacopo. 'I was afraid I might have to go to Dumbarton, or across country to Irvine.'

'Not at all,' Thomas smiled. 'You can always get a boat down the Clyde from the Broomy Lhaw at the Glasgow Fair.'

THE BATTLE OF GLASGOW CROSS

Towards the end of the thirteenth century the glittering armour and pikes of the knights and soldiers of Edward the First of England, 'Hammer of the Scots', were surging like a bloody tide across Scotland, leaving the marks of the invaders' lash on the captive's back. Wherever they went the terror of them went first, but one man stood like a rock in their path, Sir William Wallace, Laird of Elderslie and Auchinbothie.

History and legend tell of the courage of Wallace, of his great two-handed sword, of castles stormed and strongholds won, like the battle at Glasgow Cross, another goad to the ungovernable rage of Edward the First.

The west wind drove the rain onto the high ground of the Meikle Cowcaldanes, sweeping across the steep-roofed town of Glasgow in writhing sheets of icy grey and coiling in nets of mist about the brittle spire of the Cathedral. Gaunt and silent, the eyeless face of the castle walls brooded over the little town, and in the great hall Bishop Beck of Durham sat by a crackling fire while his soldiers shivered in the outhouses or kept watch on the slippery battlements.

Crouched down behind a hedge on the high ground, two badly-dressed soldiers peered through the drifting squalls to the windswept town below. The streets were deserted, and from their vantage point they could see the flagstones and the cobbles near the Cathedral glisten briefly as a stray shaft of sunlight pierced the grey clouds racing overhead. Just as quickly as it had come, the gleam was shut off, and a watchful gloom closed in again over the embattled town by the Clyde.

Crouching in a puddle behind a hawthorn bush, Andrew watched an ant sheltering behind a twig from the clear rain falling steadily from the lowering sky. 'Even that wee beast's got mair sense than we have,' he said glumly, sneezing violently. 'I never knew that men could live under water.' He stirred uncomfortably.

'Get down, ye daftie,' whispered his companion Matthew urgently. 'Do you want the English to see us?'

'Not at all,' Andrew answered, 'but if they could, they would be fish, and so would we, for that matter.' He blinked as rain ran down his leather helmet and into his eyes. 'Pauvre moi, Dieu sauve le ramenant!' he said, sneezing again.

'Och, talk Scots will ye?' said Matthew, 'Keep that for the Masters.'

In the distance a lonely sentry paced backwards and forwards on the castle battlements.

'Aye well,' Matthew spoke again, 'between the French and the Scots, the English and the Gaels, this is a Toor of Babylon gettin'. But we were telt to keep watch, so let's leave the chatter aside.'

'But the order was if any more English came over the bridge we were to send word right away,' Andrew said stubbornly. 'And what about the others?' he went on. 'I canna see hide nor hair of them and we . . .' Suddenly the world went dark, and he slumped down into the ditch behind. 'What did you do that for?' he said to Matthew angrily. 'My helmet's on well enough without you pulling it over my eyes.'

'Will you keep down, damn you?' whispered Matthew urgently, offering no apology. 'Look!'

Andrew pulled himself up the muddy bank cautiously and peered across the valley. With a clatter of hooves that could be heard even from where they lay hidden, the squat shapes of the English heavy cavalry were making their way under the great arch in the castle wall. With a 'clang' that echoed through the hills and startled the rooks from their nests in the lands of Gorbaldis the portcullis of Glasgow Castle closed fast.

The great warhorse was restless. He had been standing still

beneath the trees for several hours, and the spiked face-plate, flank mail, and ring of bronze discs hanging about his chest, together more than three pages could lift, were getting too heavy even for the mount of Sir John de Graham.

The knight sat square in his saddle, a heavy-boned man with a raw, bleak colour in his cheeks. He was dressed from head to foot in a close-fitting suit of steel armour, another burden that his steed was born to carry as they charged together, a mountain of flesh and iron, into the wavering ranks of any enemy.

'They must be in position by now,' Sir John said with a sound like a sword scraping across stone, as he turned slightly towards his companion.

'And we must wait until they are, John. There's nothing else for it,' answered the horseman beside him.

The man who had spoken was dressed in a long hooded coat of chain mail that reached from the crown of his head to below his knees. A full beard flowed down across the rippling steel circlets, and hanging from between his shoulder blades, taller than its owner, an enormous broadsword waited in its black scabbard. The man's eyes surveyed the scene, shading themselves with thought. 'And when they are,' he went on with quiet determination, 'we strike again! And then we can fight our way to some dry inn.' He laughed.

'By that time I will be stiff as stone,' answered Sir John ruefully. 'I'm beginning to think that this damned iron is married to my skin.'

Sir William Wallace looked at him and laughed grimly. 'Good Sir John,' he said. 'I would marry my steel, and yours, to other skins. Be patient. As soon as Auchinleck is in place by the Drygait we move to feint at the Castle.'

'If the Drygait of Glasgow is as dry as this wood, then he is probably swimming his way there now,' said Sir John.

'After the bridge they had to come round by the lands of Barras Yett and Eglischemeis Croft, all within sight of Edward's spies, so we must wait.'

'Aye. Aye, I know that,' agreed Sir John. 'And with luck we should . . .'

Before he could finish speaking Wallace rounded on him. 'Luck?' he cried angrily. 'There's no "luck" about it! Just courage! Courage and this ...!' He reached behind him and, with a sound like meltwater rushing down a glen, unsheathed his enormous sword and held it above him.

The other horsemen and footsoldiers watching and waiting in the sodden forest drew their weapons also or waved their pikes about and shouted, 'The Wallace! Wallace!'

The clamour was cut short as a man, sweating in spite of the chill downpour, crashed and leaped through the ferns towards them.

Before he could speak, Wallace called out to him: 'Yes?'

The messenger gasped and nodded, too breathless to say anything.

Spurring his horse forward, Wallace cried, 'Glasgow! To Glasgow!' and his army poured through the forest while the rain made puddles of their deep footprints.

When the sentries on the Bishop's Tower saw the Scots riding towards the castle gate, bold as bronze, they could hardly believe their luck. Unprotected and in the open, the small party would prove easy meat for the Bishop of Durham's battle-hardened cavalry and bowmen. The alarum spread through the fortress, and the crash of iron-shod feet running down the spiral staircases mingled with the clash of men arming themselves and the groaning of squires straining to seat their heavily-armed masters in their saddles.

The portcullis opened slowly and Edward's cavalry thundered out into the High Street. They collided with the Scots, and at once the air was filled with the cries of men and horses and the ringing peal of metal beating on metal. Wallace shouted his defiance as he swung his sword in an arc about him, and the Northumbrian foot-soldiers pushed and struck with their pikes, but kept their distance. The Scots were fighting desperately now and more than one shield had become a pin-cushion for the English archers. Backs towards the Clyde, Wallace and his men were slowly retreating towards Glasgow Cross.

As the Scots reached the point where the High Street crossed the Dumbarton to Lanark road within sight of the grove of trees by the Ladywell to the east, Sir John de Graham's squire blew several blasts on a well-travelled hunting horn, and as the clear notes faded on the wind there were answering calls from further down the hill, between the Deanside Well and the Blackfriars Monastery, and to the east near the Drygait Port.

Within minutes it became clear that the warlike Bishop Beck had been trapped between the hammer and the anvil, as the foot soldiers of Auchinleck surged from two directions and charged into the melee. They hacked their way towards the figure of Wallace who stood with his back to the Merkat Cross, swinging his two-handed sword in front of him like a scythe through a field of barley.

'Well met!' roared Wallace as his uncle Auchinleck stormed through the thick of the fight towards him, the flailing hooves of the old man's maddened charger wreaking havoc among the retreating soldiers.

'Well met indeed,' echoed the ageing Auchinleck. 'I was getting tired of waiting there in the backside of the toune, so I came to see if you needed some help, nephew.'

'If you have the time, uncle,' grinned Wallace, as his knights rode past him up the High Street after the fleeing enemy. 'And it looks as if today we have the victory,' he added happily.

'You have the victory,' echoed his uncle, fending off the departing thrust of a last Northumbrian pikeman. 'You are a good lad, William.'

'And knighted as well,' smiled Wallace.

'Yes, yes. "Sir William" then,' said his uncle. 'Sir William Wallace, Hammer of the English!'

TAKE A LETTER, OLD WILLIAM

In the year 1454 Glasgow's University, housed in the old Chapter-House of Luss in the Rottenrow, was barely four years old. New University buildings were planned to the south of the Blackfriars Monastery, but classes were still held in the damp, cramped old halls in those days when men thought the stars were made of gold and nailed to the crystal sphere of heaven.

One fine spring morning by the banks of the Molendinar, linen lay spread out and bleaching on the broad flat stones, and the clear sound of women's laughter filled the air.

But Maggie Dunlop was not laughing. She was 'black affronted'. 'I never said that at all,' she complained, but her neighbour Mary Bogle was shaking so much with amusement that she couldn't keep up the rhythm of trampling her cloth in the stream.

'But imagine sayin' that about anybody,' she giggled.

'That's just her though,' Maggie frowned. 'It wisna' me sent thon tinker to her door,' she went on. 'If she wants pots patched up, she can stop a tinker man at the merket hersel'. And as for that man of hers ...'

'Och yes,' Mary agreed sympathetically, stifling a smile. 'She's just a bisom that. And another thing. Her man was never at the cow fair at Lanark at all. Do you ken where he was that Saturday?'

'No?' said Maggie with renewed interest.

'He was in the jougs,' Mary answered triumphantly. 'They had him in the public lockholes,' she went on, tossing her head as her blue-black hair fell over her eyes.

'But what fur did they lock him up?' Maggie asked.

'For drinkin'!' Mary replied. 'And the Burgess said that he was comin' to be the worst in the hale toon!'

'That would take some doin',' answered Maggie. 'And

who was the Burgess that sent him doon? There's that many grand folk with this new University, and the Bishop's Court gettin' like a Palace, I've lost track of them.'

Mary bent down to lift her linen out of the stream. 'I don't know, dear. It's not this new wan, anyway.'

Maggie clambered onto the bank to get another shirt to wash. 'What new wan?' she asked. 'They're all new.'

'Och, this Provtest,' said Mary, twisting her cloth over the river till her knuckles whitened and the water ran down her arms. 'This new man that's over the other Burgesses in the Bishop's Council. He's called "Provtest" or "Provat" or somethin'.'

'Oh!' answered Maggie. 'You mean "Provest".'

'Aye, that wan,' Mary said, a little doubtfully.

'You mean that Sir John Steuart of Minto that's been made up,' her friend said knowledgeably.

'Well I knew that,' said Mary, turning away. 'Everybody knows that!'

Sir John Steuart of Minto was having trouble tying the ribbon at the front of his gown. The knot kept coming undone as he paced up and down, in and out of the sunlight lancing in through the open shutters.

'Help me, daughter!' he cried in anguish as the tie-ribbon broke at last and the fur-lined cape started to slip from his shoulders.

Sir John Steuart's daughter hurried into the room. She was more at ease here in the town house than in the country tower where her father was laird. Glasgow for her was full of life and bustle, the enchantment and clatter of a growing mercantile town.

'Now don't panic, father,' she said reassuringly. 'It's only old William the Scribe.'

'William is also a Regent at the University,' her father answered testily, 'and high in the favour of Lord Bishop Turnbull. Who was it replied to King James' letter of the Great Seal, eh? Answer me that!'

'I don't know, father,' said the girl, fumbling with the ribbon. 'And please keep still!'

17

'Well I'll tell you,' continued her father, lifting his chin while she tucked his collar in at the back. 'It was "old" William, that's who.' His daughter busied herself with the edge of his cloak. 'It was the man you call "old" William, girl,' he said again. 'Glasgow University has privileges equal to St. Andrews now, and we are high in the favour of King James and the Pope, and when either of them opens a letter from Glasgow, it will have been quilled in the hand of that same "old" William.'

'Oh do keep still,' said his daughter.

'There was no University in my young days, you know,' he said. 'If there had been I would have attended it. I might even have learned to write. It would be quite useful for a Provost of Glasgow to be able to write, but then ...'

'Oh father, you do go on about things,' said his daughter, brushing specks of dust from his puffed velvet sleeves. 'There we are now,' she said. 'You are fit for anyone. If the King himself should push aside that tapestry and walk in here, you need not be ashamed.'

'Don't say that,' answered Sir John nervously. 'I've got enough on my mind without your imaginings, girl.'

'Well you're ready, father,' she said. 'Off you go now.'

'Do you think the Bishop will agree?' he asked her. 'Agree to my offer, I mean,' he added.

'Father, father,' smiled the girl, shaking her head. 'You know I know nothing of politics or statecraft. Old ... I mean Scribe William, Regent William, will write your words to him well and with a flourish. Are you not in the Bishop's favour?'

'Well, yes,' answered Sir John thoughtfully. 'I am, I hope, but I hold a high and new office, and Turnbull has other matters to consider.'

'The world's estimation of you will match your own,' smiled the girl. 'I believe in you.'

'You have become a wise head on pretty shoulders since your mother died,' said her father.

'Then take a wise old young woman's advice,' laughed his daughter. 'Go, and go now, before the rain comes on.

You look like a prince. On ye go.' And with that, she bustled the anxious man towards the door.

William the Scribe sat by the window at his high sloping desk. A handful of pens stood tempering in a bowl of hot sand. He pulled one out and looked at it closely, then reached across for his penknife and began to split the end of the quill neatly down the centre and chamfer the tip.

He had just picked up a second quill when there was a rap at the sturdy door of his cell. 'Come,' he said without looking up.

Sir John Steuart of Minto lifted the latch and walked in.

'Well well, Master Minto,' he said with a smile. 'You look in fine mettle today.'

'Do I?' asked Sir John, slightly flustered. 'I've had a time this morning, William, and no mistake. I went into a room below to ask for you and there was a class in session. The talk was all of Aristotle and the seven worlds. When I opened the door you would have thought I had come from the moon.' He shook his head.

'That, my friend, is the modern world,' said the scribe. 'We have Rhetoric, Logic, Music, the full tally, all the subjects to fit a young man for Church or State. And there are great things stirring abroad, or so I believe. Some of this Italian and German learning will change the world out of all recognition before long – you mark my words.'

'I don't think I like too much change, at least not all at once,' replied Sir John unhappily.

'But it's prestige too,' urged the scribe, 'It gives your town, our town, a better name in the world at large. Now I believe you have some words for my Lord Bishop, Provost Minto?'

'That's exactly it, William: "Provost"! Now that I've been honoured with this new office, I feel I should make some, well, gesture on my own part to the Bishop and, of course, for the repose of my immortal soul.'

'Of course, of course,' agreed William, 'but give me a moment. I'm treasuring these pens, you know, John. The University has taken that many that there is a shortage of good goose feather and swan.'

'There's plenty up at Hogganfield Loch,' said Sir John.

'Oh, aye,' answered the monk, raising his eyebrows. 'I can just see myself creeping about by the Bishop's Loch, pulling feathers out of the erses of his geese and swans by the handfu'. Just the thing for a Regent of the Collegium, I'm sure.'

'I'll see what I can do about that,' John Steuart replied anxiously. 'I have plenty of geese on my estate you know.'

'Thank you,' smiled the monk. 'Another time. Be at ease John. A letter to the Bishop willna' hurt you.'

'But will he accept my gift, do you think?' Sir John asked.

'My Lord the Bishop, unless he has changed overnight, always accepts gifts,' answered William with a grimace. 'But on you go. I can take it down as you dictate.'

Sir John Steuart looked up at the ceiling and hesitated.

'Come on now, John,' urged the old scribe gently.

Sir John took a deep breath and began to dictate. 'I, Sir John Minto,' he began, then paused. 'I, I . . .'

The scribe chewed the end of his pen and stared absently out of the window.

'Are you putting this down?' Sir John asked him anxiously.

'You haven't started yet,' said William.

'I Sir John Steuart of Minto,' the nervous man began again, 'first Provost of Glasgow.' He paused. 'And Dalswinton,' he said. 'Put "Dalswinton" in there William.'

'Aye, aye,' replied the scribe curtly. 'But what comes after "Provost of Glasgow"?'

'Oh,' Sir John grinned sheepishly. 'Aye. I Sir John . . . sorry, I said that, William.' He continued, 'first Provost of Glasgow, do gift a back land and tenement to the Bishop's patrimony that for my soul's repose great St. Mungo's Bell be rungen loud . . .'

'That would be some sight,' smiled the old scribe, scratching away with his pen furiously, 'The Provost of Glasgow ringing St. Mungo's Bell.'

NO ROAD BACK

In 1513, the days of the 'Eternal Alliance' between Scotland and France, the largest ship in the world, the 240-foot *Great Michael*, mighty flagship of the Scottish navy, had sailed with all her slings and falcons, serpentines, culverins, hackbutts, crossbows and rams to the aid of the French King and the intended ruin of Henry VIII. The country was preparing for war, and in Glasgow the Provost and his Council sharpened their swords and dusted off their armour. Prayers were said for a war that was to be fought in England and in faraway places, and there was a saying at that time that there was 'no place sae far that there was never a road back'. That was before the Battle of Flodden.

The fields of corn below Stirling looked grey and unfit for reaping in the failing light as the King thundered past. Two Councillors of the Realm rode after him, desperate in their attempt to gain their Lord's attention.

Suddenly, King James reined his horse in savagely and confronted the two men. The horse stopped so abruptly that one of the men almost slipped from his saddle. James smiled briefly, but just as quickly hid his amusement, frowning at the two uneasy courtiers. Their eyes flickered nervously across the landscape, unwilling to catch their King's gaze.

'God's blood!' roared the King. 'Is this a hunt or a Royal Council? Did I not say leave me be!?'

'B . . . but my Liege,' stammered the nearest man. 'We have only your needs and the Kingdom's in our minds.'

'I am the Kingdom,' said James coldly.

'We had no wish to pursue you, my lord,' said the man.

'Then why the devil did you?' The King stretched his shoulders stiffly. 'I've had a hard ride to hounds today. When you came up on me I thought by your speed you had sighted the white hind. Instead, the deer we had flushed is gone and I, I don't mind telling you my Lords, am no longer in the humour I was in this morning. Be brief!' He stared at them, picking impatiently at his gloves.

'My Lord,' said one of the Councillors, plucking up courage. 'Word's come from Leith that your brother King Henry has sailed for France.'

James' cheeks, red from the biting wind, grew even rosier and one hand held the other tightly, as if to stop it leaping up and doing damage to the air. 'Very well,' he said quietly, so quietly that the two men had to lean forward to hear what he said. 'So that's how his ship sails is it? He attacks my ships. He kills my Warden of the Marches, he joins with the Holy League against Our Cousin France. Well, well. Henry's gone to the wars you say?'

'Yes, my Liege,' the man replied.

'Then We shall go to war also,' James said grimly. 'I have thirteen ships of three tops, ten smaller, and two more under repair. I will carry this war to England. We'll need the guns from Edinburgh and a muster of all the army.'

'But my Lord,' protested the Councillors together. 'Each of the great cannon will take thirty-six oxen to pull . . . You said, to England?'

'To England, you fools!' the King replied, flying into a rage. 'To where else? To the moon?' And with that he spurred his horse and rode off in the direction of Stirling Castle. His two Councillors rode after him, but this time they were in no hurry to catch up.

The Earl of Lennox, Lord Provost of Glasgow, had a beard that would have made fresh snow look grey, but for all that his thick bull-neck and his long arms were as strong as a man twenty years his junior. He stood legs apart and arms folded as the courtyard slowly filled up with the men who had come in answer to his message. He turned to the man standing in the doorway beside him. 'Well John,' he asked, 'are they all here?'

John Steuart looked about the courtyard for familiar faces. 'Aye, your Grace,' he said at last. 'Bailies and

Burghers all. The Council of Glasgow ready to ride off to war.'

'Oho! Not ready, not even armed,' said the Earl with a snort. 'Each man's to muster here at Glasgow Castle the morn's morn in full armour with their grooms, pages, baggage attendants and suchlike, and foot soldiers and other riff-raff with pikes and billhooks in the street beyond. And, John . . .,' he added as an afterthought, 'send me my armourer.'

In a little while the armourer and his apprentice wheeled out Lennox' armour on its wooden mannikin. The figure was dressed as the Earl himself would be in battle, chest piece and skirt of metal hoops, leg and arm pieces, joints, greaves, all worn on top of a hauberk of chain mail and a padded coat.

'Where's my helmet?' asked Lennox.

The apprentice scurried back into the castle, emerging minutes later staggering under the weight of an enormous gryphon-crested helmet.

The Earl poked thoughtfully at the padded jerkin showing along the edge of the breastplate. 'I must be with the King in Edinburgh in two days. What of my horse's armour? Will that be ready also?'

'Gervase?' said William the armourer, cuffing his apprentice across the ear. 'Don't stand there chewing the cud, boy! Is the Master's caparison ready for his horse?'

The glazed expression on Gervase's face turned to one of blank surprise. 'Oh aye, Master William,' he stammered. 'There's just a wee bit to tool round the edge, and . . .'

'I think there are too many masters in this town,' interrupted Earl Lennox. 'There had better be no "wee bits" to do when the herald blows, that's all.'

Suddenly all heads turned as a commotion erupted by the entrance to the long straw-lined passage that led from the stables to the inner courtyard.

'What the devil?' said Lennox angrily, striding forward.

'It's your horse, my Lord,' said the armourer.

Confusion reigned as Lennox arrived on the scene. A groom was lying on the ground clutching at his shoulder and two others were dancing about the great beast like leaves in a flood as the war-charger plunged and kicked, flailing blindly with hooves that could knock down a wall.

'He's been like this all day, my Lord,' gasped one of the grooms. 'We canna understand it. Boran's no' a high-strung nag.'

'Well we will all be high strung if we are not in Edinburgh on the appointed day,' answered Earl Lennox grimly.

At the sound of his voice the enormous beast grew calmer. 'There will be a few changes in Glasgow when this war is over,' stormed the Provost, giving his kinsmen and his servants a baleful look.

Two days later, when the company, some 150 strong, marched over the Molendinar, the day was clear and still. Bright armour glittered and the spears and halberds were like a small forest of steel, tightly packed behind the Lord as he led them towards the east.

Just beyond the Butts, Earl Lennox paused and looked back at the town as the gates clanged shut. The sense of unease that he felt was reflected in the continued restlesness of his horse. 'Well,' he said quietly at last. 'That's Glasgow. Now, where's this war?'

As King James stood on Flodden Edge he could see the desperate struggle that was taking place beside the Branx Bridge. Ever since he had had word that the Earl of Surrey had crossed the Twizel Bridge to the north, he had seen the fickle tides of war begin to turn against the army of Scotland. Borthwick, the master-gunner, had implored him to fire on the bridge and destroy it, and now the Earl of Angus had come to him with the same request, but the King was stubborn in his refusal. 'To fire on the bridge now would give us an unfair advantage over the English,' he said. 'I'll not take a victory by losing my honour.'

'But my Lord King,' protested Angus. 'This is war, not a matter of chivalry! My Lord,' he implored. 'I beg you . . .'

'If you are afraid,' the King answered slowly, 'then Angus, you may gang hame.'

The proud Angus looked sadly at his king for the last time. The advancing English were now pouring into the valley towards the Scots on the sloping, slippery ground. Apart from the occasional 'boom' of a cannon, the field of battle had become strangely silent as men grappled with men in a struggle that might well mean the end of a king, or even a nation.

'Then I'll gang,' said Angus slowly. 'Have I your leave, my Liege?'

James turned his head haughtily and Angus went to join his kinsmen and followers, but the red tide of Surrey's hordes was drawing closer.

'Lennox? Where is Lennox?' shouted the King as smoke from the Scots cannon blew back on the watching lairds.

'Here my Lord,' answered the Provost of Glasgow.

'Lennox, I myself will lead the vanguard down to the battle,' James said with an air of finality.

'My Lord?' gasped the Earl in disbelief.

'I will have no opposition in this,' James thundered.

'There's little time, my Lord,' answered the Earl of Lennox wearily. 'They are already over the river to our left.'

James sagged visibly, like a man aged by a bad dream.

As the tide of battle swept closer and the day wore on, the voice of the Earl of Lennox could be heard, raised above the grim struggle on the slippery hill. 'The King!' he cried. 'Hold fast about the King!'

When night fell on the Scottish Borders, and the Tweed and the Till rushed down to the sandy shores of the sea, the waters were darker than usual. One member of every great family of Scotland lay dead about their King and his son; and on the field of Flodden even the Provost of Glasgow was numbered among that terrible harvest of the flowers of their age plucked in the dark forests of war.

MARY QUEEN OF DARNLEY

Mid-sixteenth-century Scotland was a land with a troubled monarchy, a land of plots and counter-plots and murder in the night. One evening in 1566 Henry Darnley, self-styled 'King of the Realm', lay in bed in his father's house in Glasgow, fighting the pain that had been growing in his stomach since supper.

It was a year since that dreadful March night when the Queen's Italian Secretary and favourite Rizzio had been stabbed to death in front of her by Moray, Morton, and that same Darnley who now lay twisting and turning and trying to ignore the increasing pain. Although he had dismissed the Parliament, declared for the Protestant cause and proclaimed himself King, there was little thought of royal pomp as he reached for the water beside his bed with a shaking hand.

Beads of cold sweat stood out on his forehead as he seemed to see the face of his wife, the Queen, floating in the air of the darkened room like a picture painted on cobwebs. 'Mary!' he moaned. 'Mary!'

But the vision would not go away, and hung there, a waking dream in the gloomy room.

After the violent death of her secretary, Mary had escaped and gathered an army to protect her. She had tried, and tried hard, to heal the breach with the nobles after the birth of her son James, but Darnley had remained a petulant and spoilt adolescent who would have none of her. His constant plots and intrigues had made him almost universally hated, and he had moved to his father's house on the Stable Green near Glasgow Cathedral.

Matthew Darnley, 12th Earl of Lennox and father of the sick man, was an old aristocrat of stern character. His grandfather, 10th Earl of Lennox, had died in battle at

Flodden; his brother was Captain of French Gendarmerie in Avignon; and his son Henry was a debauched assassin.

He peered into the face of that son with a mixture of bitterness and concern. 'Keep still, son,' he said. 'That's best with the smallpox.'

'But it's so cold, father,' shivered his son, adding, 'It's not the smallpox. I know it isn't.'

The Earl straightened up and looked away. 'As your Majesty pleases,' he said slowly.

Darnley lifted himself on an elbow and stared angrily at his father. 'Majesty?' he sneered. 'Majesty? This "Majesty" has a belly that's on fire.' The sudden effort made him slump back on the bolster. 'It's Crawford I want,' he gasped. 'Thomas Crawford! If her physician comes, send him away. Nae mair doctors!'

Earl Lennox turned and looked out of the window and across the square to Provand's Lordship. 'I should have called ye Absalom,' he said quietly as he left the room.

Darnley dreamed. He was standing in a garden at night, and huge ravens or bats flew above the ruins of a building still smoking from the fire or explosion that had destroyed it. His favourite page boy stood some way off with his back towards him. Suddenly a woman's voice cried out in French, 'Laissez-le tranquille! Rizzio! Rizzio!' The page boy turned round slowly. The whiteness of his fleshless skull gleamed pale as his nightshirt and a wisp of red hair fell across an eyeless socket. Darnley cried out till his throat hurt, but there was no sound.

'My Lord!' said Thomas Crawford anxiously, shaking him by the shoulder. 'All's well, Your Majesty.'

'Don't call me that,' Darnley answered, coughing. He sat up suddenly and looked at Crawford, wild-eyed. 'That bitch has poisoned me,' he gasped. 'I'm tellin' you Tom.'

'Of course Your M . . . my Lord,' answered Crawford, humouring him.

Darnley was shouting now, waving his arms about in a frenzy. 'They made me stick that wee rat Rizzio,' he continued. 'But she was askin' for it, beggin' for it. Why did she have to watch me dae it?' He burst into tears. 'They

27

held her arms and forced her to watch,' he sobbed.

'Shhh . . . my Lord,' said Crawford consolingly.

Darnley reached across and took hold of Crawford by the lace on his collar.

'You're ch . . . choking me, my L . . . Lord,' gurgled the man, trying to prise Darnley's fingers away from his neck.

'I dissolved Parliament, didn't I?' roared Darnley. 'So, I must be King, eh? The King's a King,' he raved in his delirium. ' "The Queen's in Stirling Castle-o", but she's no. She's out! She says she's pardoned us all, but who is King, her or me? Ohhh!' he moaned. 'I'm no' weel.'

Crawford managed to free himself from the grasping fingers at his throat. 'Be calm my Lord. Lie back now.'

Darnley collapsed backwards with a sigh, but sat bolt upright as a sudden hammering on the door of the room was followed by cries of 'Open for Her Majesty!'

Henry Darnley glimpsed the door being flung open by a tall Switzer with a polished helmet, and as he squeezed his eyes tight shut and pretended to be asleep he heard the soft, quick steps of a woman crossing the tiled floor.

'Leave Us, Thomas Crawford,' Mary said with calm dignity. 'We'd be alone with Our husband.'

As Crawford backed out of the room, Mary looked down at her husband, fighting with himself to be still in spite of his discomfort. 'Henry,' she said sadly. 'Must you always pretend? Have you nothing to say to me?'

His eyes snapped open, like a fox watching the hunt go by its den. 'I'm dying,' he said. 'Is that not enough?'

She pulled the sheets away from his chin angrily. 'For the love of Christ sit up and be a man, Henry,' she snapped.

'You hate me!' he said petulantly, turning away.

Mary shook her head and took off her gloves. 'No,' she answered. 'Not "hate". I don't hate you, Henry. I hate what you have done. You are not ill, you are afraid, and there's no medicine against fear.'

'I am sick,' Darnley wailed. 'Mary, if you could only feel the pain as I do.'

She stepped back as if struck in the face. 'Pain?' she cried. 'Pain? The pain of plots? The pain of seeing those you love and trust murdered before your very eyes by your very husband. Oh yes, my Lord Henry Darnley, I can feel the pain.'

'But you know what I mean,' he answered awkwardly, 'and you've pardoned us all.'

Mary Stuart reached out and took hold of one of the carved uprights supporting the heavy canopy over the bed. 'Henry,' she said wearily. 'If you must know, it is I who feel unwell, sick of the violence that plagues this land. You called yourself "King", but to rule it is I who must be the man.' She turned to go. 'I'm lodged not forty paces from here in the Laird of Provan's House. Perhaps you will be in a more reasonable frame of mind tomorrow.'

'No!' he cried, sitting upright. 'No, Mary, wait!'

The Queen of Scots looked back at the dishevelled figure of her husband. 'Yes?' she asked coldly.

'Mary!' said Darnley, his voice breaking. 'Mary, I didn't mean . . .'

'Oh be a man, Henry,' she replied without looking round. 'You declared yourself once,' and at her light tap the door was opened and she left him alone again.

'I was man enough to father your whelp James,' he called, after the door was safely closed again. 'Man enough to declare myself King!' As the fire burned low he felt himself slipping once again into the garden of the ravens and the bats.

As Mary walked back to Provand's Lordship with her escort, the sun was already setting downriver and the Cathkin Braes across the valley were dark like cardboard cutouts pasted on a stained-glass window. Little copses of trees, black against the sky, reminded her of animals and faces, but then the day-dream slipped away into thoughts of the menace of real things and the treachery and lies that cast darker shadows across the Royal House of Scotland than the hills about Glasgow.

Later that evening, as she rested in her chamber, the shutters closed against the night and Joseph, brother of the murdered Rizzio, seated at her feet, she felt more secure, but very, very tired. At her elbow stood a tall glass of

Falernian wine and in her lap, the place marked by a slim finger, the poems of William Dunbar.

'Joseph, Joseph!' she said to the man at her feet. 'What's to become of me?'

His lute made a hollow sound as he leaned it against the side of her chair. 'What shall become of you, my Lady?' he asked. 'What would you like to become of you? Nothing, surely, for you could not be more becoming.'

She smiled at him. 'Unsubtle,' she laughed, 'but what I need, dear Joseph.'

'I am simply glad to be here,' he said.

'So was my poor Rizzio, your brother,' answered Mary quietly. She shuddered and closed her book. 'No. I will put that behind me,' she said. 'You are like a breath of sunshine from warmer days, my dear friend, and I have not many of those. There are so many, many enemies all about me. Scotland treats me like a foreigner, the man Knox preaches terrible things against me.'

Joseph snapped his fingers. 'That for the man Knox,' he grinned.

Mary giggled and sipped her wine. 'If it were that easy,' she replied. 'But my husband behaves like a spoilt and vicious child. He is swayed this way and that by the violent and the ignorant, by Huntly, Argyll, Lethington and the rest. Is there to be no peace at all? Anywhere? Ever?'

Joseph Rizzio looked at the face of the pale, intelligent woman, her eyes dark with unwanted memories. The candles flickered suddenly and Mary looked up, startled.

'Perhaps,' Joseph said slowly, 'If he were in truth dead, why then . . .'

Although he left the rest unsaid, Mary knew what was in his mind. 'No, I'll not think of that,' she whispered. 'And you are not to either. Yet, perhaps . . .' She fingered the half-empty glass thoughtfully. 'Play for me Joseph,' she smiled, brushing the back of his hand with the tips of her fingers.

Across the square, a sick man dreamed he was in a burning house with a dead page.

THE PALE HORSEMAN

Disaster was upon the city of Glasgow, and it seemed to the people as they tried in vain in that year of 1646 to close the town gates against the hardness of the world that the horsemen of the Apocalypse themselves were thundering along the Gallowgate to Glasgow Cross. The effects of civil war and religious divisions had been made worse by a crop failure and the famine that followed. The price of grain had rocketed to an all-time high of one shilling and ninepence Scots a peck, and now a terrible visitor was in the city. No one knew where it came from, or how, but those whom it called on had white crosses painted on their doors and the only way to fight it was with fire or pitiless quarantine.

James Anderson should have been on his way to Dumbarton to see about Irish linen, but when his friend Rob Rowan met him in the High Street, he was standing quite still, his face troubled.

'Good morn' to ye James,' said Rob as he approached. 'I thought you would be well away by now!'

James Anderson looked up as his friend approached. 'Aye Rob, by rights I should,' he replied. 'I just stopped for a minute because of the noise that Gilbert Mereshell's dug is makin'.' As he spoke, the sound of a mournful howling and yapping came from the nearby house.

Rob nodded. 'Right enough,' he said. 'That's a hellish row altogether. Now you come to mention it, I haven't seen the Mereshells about for a day or twa, either of them.' The sound of whining and scratching interrupted him from behind the planking door. 'It's wantin' out,' he observed. 'Maybe we should have a wee look.'

Rob pushed the door, calling out as it creaked open, 'Hallo? Mr. Mereshell?'

31

No human voice answered, but the dog raved and yammered in the darkness within.

'It sounds mair than half-starved,' said James.

'It's queer that,' agreed Rob. 'They're good with beasts.' He pushed the door fully open and walked boldly into the house.

'There's something not right in here,' whispered James as they stood in the dim hallway.

Before Rob could reply, a small terrier rushed past them and out into the street. 'The damn thing near had me over,' Rob complained as he walked down the hall. His voice filtered back to James Anderson who was still standing by the doorway. 'What a vile reek there is in here,' Rob was saying. 'It's like something deid. Are you coming in James?'

'I suppose so,' mumbled James Anderson reluctantly, but as he walked in after Rob, he was startled by his friend's sudden cries from the living room.

'Come and help us!' Rob was calling in terror. 'Ohh . . .'

James ran to help his friend, but as he entered the darkened room, he was stopped short by an over-poweringly sweet smell. 'What is it Rob?' he gagged, trying to focus his eyes in the gloom.

His friend was standing to the left, near the table that occupied the centre of the room. The table was set for a meal and he could make out the bowls ready for the broth that had never been put in them. He wondered at the piles of old clothes on the floor near the hearth.

'James,' whispered his friend, reaching out for his sleeve in the sugary blackness. 'It . . . it's the Mereshells, him and his gudewife. I've found them.'

The Chamber in the Town House had never been so full. Bailies and burghers, magistrates and merchants were all shouting at once, and those who could neither stand nor sit crowded in the doorway trying to make themselves heard.

'Gentlemen! Gentlemen!' roared Provost Potterfield in a stentorian voice, hammering on the long table with his cane. 'Calm yourselves, please! Gentlemen!' He banged so hard on the edge of the great polished table-top that his cane broke, and the noise subsided a little. 'Thank you,' he said with a grimace. 'Now. Bailie Anderson. You were saying that you yourself discovered them.'

'Well, it was Master Rowan that led me to the door,' he answered above the general muttering. 'There they were, bloated and blackened with,' and his voice became almost inaudible, 'with plague!' he said quietly.

'What's that?' someone shouted from the back.

The general uproar was in danger of breaking out again as James Anderson stood up and shouted at the top of his voice. 'I said, "Plague"!'

There was total silence.

Bailie Neilson cleared his throat nervously. 'It's a judgement, I tell ye,' he said bitterly. 'But why did it have to happen in our time?'

The Lord Provost fingered the broken end of his cane. 'Men aye say in times like this, "What have I done to deserve this?"' he replied. 'The answer is not overmuch, nor great work to prevent it, Bailie Neilson. The meeting had best know now. There's upwards of seven other cases reported this very morn about the town and in the roundabout farms.' As the hubbub began again he raised his voice above the noise and said loudly, 'If you want to know what to do about it, the answer is, I don't know.'

'Wall them up,' said a voice.

'Fire's the answer,' called another.

Provost Potterfield strode over to the window. He paused for a moment, hands behind his back, then turned and spoke again. 'I said I didn't know what to do,' he began, 'but perhaps I should have said "what not to do". I remember my grandfather telling me about the last time the plague visited Glasgow, in '72.'

'We canna do as they did then,' called a voice. 'Walling folk up in their ain hooses!'

'No,' answered the Provost slowly. 'I'm not suggesting that. But I have been looking at the minutes of this body for those days and there's a lesson for us in them. First thing is there were watchers.' He cleared his throat and began to read. '"Further, we appoint ten men to go about for sighting of the sick and deid, with full leave to peer in windies, lift any latch, and search any hearth until ye peril of ye peste be gone from our town. The searchers for the Rattenraw be on their way first, for that part of the town has many folk afflicted . . ."'

'It's the Rattenraw again,' interrupted the Water Bailie. 'That's where Anderson found the Mereshells.'

The Provost continued. 'Where was I? Oh, aye, ". . . Bread is ordered to be weel burnit afore eating, and nae meat to be sellit nigh the midden."' He stopped reading, and shut the leather-bound copy of the Council Minutes. 'They blamed the contagion on "pipers, fiddlers, minstrels, and vagabonds",' he said, 'and God knows, we have enough of them with us in this town in our own day, but we have come some way since those words I have just read were first written down. We know that it must be contained. We can do that. We also know that bad food and meats in this hot summer we have been having are something to do with it, that and the water shortage. So, the main things are to contain the disease and to see that it spreads no further.'

'Locking gates and doors is no use,' said William Neilson, 'Maybe we should fire affected parts of the town.'

'We should certainly burn the clothes and goods of them that have it, or have died of it,' agreed the Provost, 'but to burn the town would be like cutting off your feet to save yourself from walking. The first thing is to find out how bad it is and exactly *where* it is.'

There were cries of agreement, and William Neilson stepped forward. 'We need to close down these butchers at the rubbish dumps,' he said emphatically. 'You know, what they don't sell at the market they keep below their beds till the following week. That canna be very healthy. We must act quickly, and go on acting, Provost.'

'Well who is to take part?' asked the Provost.

There was an embarrassed silence.

James Anderson looked up. 'The wind brings the plague,' he said slowly.

'We canna keep out the wind,' Neilson laughed dryly. 'But we can keep out Paisley and Govan folk and the like. What do you think, Anderson?' He turned and looked at James Anderson who was sitting quietly, as if deep in thought. 'Would you mind sitting back a bittie, James,' he said, lifting a hankie to his nose.

'Sit back yourself, Neilson,' replied James Anderson angrily. 'There's nothing wrang,' he paused, adding almost inaudibly, 'with me.'

The crowded room was still and all eyes were turned on him.

'What are you all lookin' at?' he said, a note of fear in his voice.

The Provost leaned across to pat his arm then thought better of it.

'You are a bit peely wally, Anderson,' he said. 'Maybe ye ran too fast to get here with your news.'

'I'm all right,' Anderson replied in desperation.

'So was the man Mereshell and his wife till twa days ago,' the Provost answered gravely. 'I think you'd best away to your house and lock the door against visitors.'

'But I tell you I'm all right,' Anderson replied, standing up hastily. 'I should know whether I'm all right or not, whether I have the . . . whether I'm well or not.'

The Provost coughed and fingered the closed book on the table in front of him.

James Anderson backed towards the door. 'All right, all right!' he said angrily. 'I'm going then.'

'Right. Best do that James,' said Provost Potterfield quietly. 'Close the door after you.'

'Puir man,' said the Provost with a sigh.

'We have to think of the whole town,' Neilson answered with a frown. 'Not just one Bailie.' For a moment it seemed to him as if his eyes refused to focus. He sat back in his chair, startled, and shook his head to clear it. 'I'm sorry,' he said with a nervous laugh. 'For a second there I felt a wee bit dizzy. I'll be all right in a meenit. It will pass, I know it will! It's nothing, nothing at all!'

THE DEVIL-DOLLS OF POLLOCK HOUSE

One evening in the autumn of 1677 a strange and terrible event took place in the curtained shadows of a rambling old house near Glasgow. Sir George Maxwell was found dead at his imposing home in the Pollock Estate, murdered by witches.

During his life the Covenanting laird had been imprisoned, only to be released on a bond of £20,000, a vast sum in those days. The centre and the victim of intrigue, he was luckier than his friend Thomas Jackson of the Parish of Eastwood who was banished to the fields of West Flanders, sold as a slave to fight in the wars against the Spanish, escaped, and after terrible hardships and wandering, finally returned to Glasgow where, according to accounts of the day, 'He was recognized by watching men, taken after a brief and bitter struggle, and treated with great cruelty tae the loss of both his eyes.'

And while his friends were pulled down about him one by one, Sir George was left alone at last in the Great Hall of Pollock House. As the fire flickered in front of him and his black cat Endor slept on his wasted knees, it seemed to the drowsy man that he was not, after all, alone. Perhaps something nestled in the shadowy rafters of the long hall, waiting until the night became quite still, the fire died, and the laird's eyes closed in sleep at last. It may be that as the curtain of sleep was drawn across his world, something rustled above his head like dry twigs in a forgotten wood where things drop down to tear and rend and kill with fright.

Lord Justice Dalglish banged his gavel on the bench and scowled at the noisy crowd that filled his court. The noise subsided and he nodded towards the Procurator, Mr.

Blackweel. 'Read the charges, Mr. Blackwee.'

'Blackweel,' said the Procurator, ignoring the sarcasm. 'Very well, but get on with it.'

Mr. Blackweel cleared his throat, adopted a pose, and started to declaim like an actor. 'The charges against the seven wretches before us this day at Paisley. The aforementioned miscreants being, as it were, former servants to the late and murdered Sir George . . .'

He was interrupted by Lord Justice Dalglish. 'You are not to say "murdered", Mr. Blackweel,' he reminded him.

'Beg pardon, my Lord,' he said, then continued, 'The former servants of Sir George Maxwell of Pollock House stand here accused,' and he paused. 'Stand!' he roared with gusto.

The seven got shakily to their feet and the crowd made a sound like a theatre audience at the appearance of the villain.

Blackweel's legal eye swept along the line of the dishevelled, trembling prisoners. 'You are here accused,' he shouted, waving a well-manicured finger at them, 'of the foul m. . . death of said Sir George by diverse means, to wit, ye vile witchcraft!'

At the word 'witchcraft' cries of horror and disgust were heard in the packed courtroom, but Mr. Blackweel was in full flood and was not to be stopped. 'And further,' he continued, 'ye are also charged that ye did make graven images of nameless horrors and stick them through with muckle lang preens in hopes to pain said Sir George aforementioned unto deid!' He drew a deep breath and continued. 'And it is further held against you – and I can hardly believe that it is writ here and has happened in Paisley – that ye have done Satan's will and sported and danced on the Sabbath with merriment. But the last is not a capital charge m'lud,' he added, turning to look up at the rotund figure of Lord Justice Dalglish.

'I am aware of that Mr. Blackweel,' replied the judge.

As the tale of treachery, murder and the black arts unfolded, the court became hushed. Shawls were wrapped more tightly about shoulders, and men and boys avoided each other's gaze for fear they might see some strange light in an eye or a mark they had not noticed before.

It seems that when the body of the laird was found and the terrified servants fled crying 'Diels!'' and 'Witches!' they left a young girl downstairs in the huge shadowy kitchen stirring the evening broth.

She found herself alone with the mutilated body of the Baronet and, perhaps, something else as well. Some accounts say, 'This young serving woman, having heard the cries in the dark and of the dread surmise, with the heart of a lion did goe and search aboot, finding in her maister's very bedroom vile images of wax pierced through and through.'

Her testimony only served to spark off a real witch hunt, and everyone accused everyone else of dabbling in the Black Arts, but suspicion and rumour still favoured mainly the unfortunate servants of the laird.

As the old Scots proverb says, 'deid men canna sing that loud', and the ghost of the bewitched Baronet never returned to tell what tore it from his living body that night. There was, however, little doubt in the courtroom in Paisley who the culprits were, and as the servants stood quaking in their bare feet by the long bench it was with sinking hearts that they heard Mr. Blackweel thunder, 'And so, my Lord, the accused did conjure up with malice demons to kiss and nip them on their shoulders – witness the marks that have been found. As has been demonstrated by the authorities from the *Compendium Maleficarum* and the *Disquisitionum Magicarum Libri Sex* of Louvain, it's plain to me as oats in a pot that the accused did conjure a fiery man tae drap doon square on the heid of the aforementioned Sir George and gnaw upon his living banes!'

As the screams and shouts in the courtroom threatened to break out into riot, Mr. Blackweel's voice could be heard shouting over the noise, 'And the Scriptures say, "Ye shall not suffer a witch tae live!"'

Andra had a sore back. He had been carrying faggots and

kindling across Paisley Green all morning, and as he dropped his bundle on the growing pile he looked at his friend Wull resentfully. 'Is that you finished for the day then?' he asked sarcastically.

'Could be,' Wull said with a toothless grin.

'Then again, maybe ye've no' started yit,' Andra observed, straightening his back and frowning. 'I've hurt myself with all that. There's enough there, surely.'

'Suppose so,' muttered Wull with a glance at the neat row of stacked faggots stretching across the Green towards the Abbey. 'There's enough there to roast all the witches in Scotland.'

'I doubt there's enough for that in the hale of Cathay,' answered the old man.

'Aye, there's a few about,' said Wull in a low voice. 'Did you hear about thon Sybil Dowe? She sold an owl's heart to Agnes Moidart, the parish daftie, to rub on any man's shoulder to make him love her.'

'Och away,' said Andra. 'I'm past all that. Anyway, if I wisna', rubbing a second-hand owl's heart on my jacket would be just the thing, I'm sure. The daftie, ye say?'

'The daftie,' agreed Wull with finality. 'But let off on account of that and better off than them.' He gestured in the direction of the mute figures tied to the poles impaled in the heaps of kindling on the wet grass.

'It's a bit damp,' Andra remarked with a professional glance at the dewy ground. 'Are they weel strangled?'

'Oh aye,' Wull replied. 'That's sixteen pence to you.'

Somewhat mollified, Andra went for a kindled torch, leaving Wull staring at the misty town indifferently.

Andra walked along, methodically setting light to the heaps of faggots as he went. 'This wan's not going yet,' he complained. 'I knew it was on the damp side for so many.'

'Was there not mair?' asked Wull.

Andra paused, the torch sending wisps of thin blue smoke into the chilly morning air. 'Well,' he said thoughtfully, 'There was that wan that hanged himself, so that's seven, no, I'm wrang, there's the fower that escaped after the trial.'

39

'Oh aye,' Wull smiled, brightening. 'To the Hardgate or somesuch.'

Andra looked at him knowingly. 'And what else?'

Wull frowned. He didn't like games more complicated than 'Find the Lady' at the fair or peg-board with a pot of ale at his elbow. 'What are you on about, auld yin?' he asked.

'Here's what,' said the old man. 'There's six here set to burn, and another hanged, and fower got out. How many's that?'

'Do you think I'm going to tell you?' replied Wull. 'Do your own working out.'

'All right,' Andra grinned, 'That's eleven, and with the serving-wench Annabel Stewart that's twelve.'

'So it is,' answered Wull, coughing painfully. 'Brilliant! My God, what a reek! I canna abide that!'

'Aye. They're fair blazin' now,' said Andra, looking over his handiwork.

The fires had caught, and in the heart of each of the pyres flickering flames were creeping up the stakes with a ghastly inevitability. Clouds of acrid green smoke drifted across the Green and into the town, and the sound of shutters being closed in an effort to keep out the stench drifted across to them like gunfire.

'But what are you getting at?' asked Wull, rubbing his watering eyes with the back of his hand.

'Well, that's twelve,' continued the irrepressible Andra. 'And if you count the murdered laird himself, that's . . . thirteen.'

Wull's eyes opened wide in spite of the billowing smoke and ashes. 'Are you trying to tell me . . .' he began.

'I'm not trying to tell you anything,' interrupted Andra, 'but you ken the auld rhyme as well as me.'

'You'll be asking me to dance next,' coughed Wull.

'Aye, jist like the rhyme,' replied the old man.

> *Dance for joy upon the green,*
> *But ye'll dance tae Hell*
> *When there are thirteen!*

THERE'S NO SMOKE WITHOUT A BARON

For centuries after its founding Glasgow was a cluster of narrow streets about the old Merket Cross, but by the 1700s, tobacco, molasses, rum and slaves had filled the cramped alleys and lanes of the town with the bustle and business of an international port. Glasgow was a canvas painted by an artist who didn't know when to stop, so that the figures in his picture were jammed together, the buildings piled on top of one another, and every available inch of the scene filled with men, women, dogs, boxes and bales, every inch that is except the top edge of the picture, where a forest of masts, rigging and pennants marked the line of the life-giving Clyde. Port Glasgow had been founded in 1688, but the Clyde was being deepened, and in the bustling years of the seventeenth century tobacco filled the warehouses of Glasgow to bursting, and the merchants who imported it, the great barons of the weed, strutted in their finery along the Plain Stanes of Glasgow while the Tron Steeple rang its chimes across the town.

The 'Tobacco Barons' were a tight-knit cabal allied by business and marriage, and William Cunningham, John Glassford and Alexander Spiers together controlled over half the trade into and through Glasgow, and seven and a half million tons of profitable goods equals dedicated and ruthless men.

The street by the Cross was thronged with people. Barefoot children splashed in and out of the puddles, calling each other names, and sailors trying to get their land-legs walked with an uneasy gait towards the gin-shops of the Bridgegait. Busy and noisy as the street was, one part of it was free of traffic. Down the right hand side of the Trongait, passing under the arch of a church and fetching up by the Cross itself, stretched a broad area of paved ground, the only part of any street that was paved in the whole of Glasgow. Citizens and strangers alike avoided it, but the tall man who strolled along it confidently seemed unaware of that and perfectly at his ease. In his tricorn hat with his scarlet-lined cape billowing out behind him, he looked both proud and formidable; a prince, or at any rate, a merchant prince. Some distance behind him, staggering under the weight of an enormous trunk, his African servant struggled to keep up with him. John Glassford was on his way to his morning counting-house.

Suddenly an urchin darted out from an alley, colliding with the stately figure and almost knocking him off balance.

'Out of my way, boy,' snarled John Glassford.

'I didna' see ye,' the mite replied sarcastically.

A silver-topped cane landed on the boy's head with a resounding crack.

'Ooya, ma heid!' he cried, rubbing his matted hair.

'The Plain Stanes are the province of the tobacco merchants,' said Glassford haughtily. 'Be off with you!'

He raised his cane again, but the lad ran off with cries of 'I'm as good as you, so I am,' and 'Lairdie! Lairdie!'

John Glassford looked behind to see that Walter was still following with his kist of precious papers, and continued on his way.

'Well, well,' laughed William Cunningham as he walked up to Glassford. 'You gave that urchin his licks and no mistake.'

'Ach, these people must be taught respect, William,' John Glassford replied seriously. 'Are we making this town or are we not?'

William Cunningham smiled, stepping to one side as the sweating Walter drew level with his master and put the trunk down on the paving-stones. 'How's your Caribbean venture, John?' asked Cunningham slyly.

'What? Oh, the Caribbean,' Glassford replied with a start. 'The boy has all the papers relating to that in my box. Haven't you Walter?'

'Oh yes, Mister Glassford, sir,' said Walter with alacrity.

'I was thinking of one of these African boys myself, John,' said William Cunningham. 'Does he work well?'

'Oh he's good and strong,' replied Glassford as if Walter was not there. 'Chosen special for me he was, from a West African voyage, and not for sale, I may add.'

'Must be reliable then,' said Cunningham, nodding. 'Still, slaves, tobacco, goods, it's a golden triangle right enough. Can't complain I suppose, eh John?'

'We could do with transporting some of these roughnecks out of the Fiddler's Close and off the High Street. It's like a regular underground den of thieves up there. Something must be done you know, William.'

William Cunningham shrugged his shoulders. 'What can we do? Short of troops or demolition they are hid away fast in there. Still, some of the Bridewell women are away. Quite a few of my captains make up their ballast with the women they get for a few shillin' and then sell them to indentures in America.'

'Best place for them,' Glassford replied. 'Wouldn't go to the Colonies meself of course. The reports I get back from the trading posts west of Boston, Newport, Providence and the like beggar description. The red men have taken to lifting hair you know.'

'What do you mean?' asked Cunningham in surprise. 'Is that some new custom?'

'So I believe,' answered Glassford gravely, 'but it means cutting it off, and most of the, you know, up here,' he added, pointing to the top of his head. 'Called "scalping" I believe. Barbarous anyway.'

'Aye, the price of tobacco is dear sometimes,' agreed Cunningham sagely. 'Still, as I said, we canna complain, and we have our position and our dignity.'

'A man should never lose his dignity,' agreed John Glassford. He turned to the patiently waiting Walter. 'Come on boy,' he said curtly, 'I didn't buy you to stand about all day. There's business to be done.'

'I'll not keep you,' Cunningham grinned as John Glassford strutted off towards his counting-room.

The office that the great John Glassford hired on a daily

43

basis was a small room near the top of a tenement by the East Port. It was a long climb up narrow stairs, and by the time they reached their landing, both Glassford and the long-suffering Walter were panting and walking slowly.

'Put the box down by the window,' gasped John Glassford. His servant struggled across the room and dumped the chest on the bare floorboards with a loud crash.

'I said be careful,' John Glassford shouted angrily, 'and shut that window, laddie.'

Walter looked flustered. 'Sorry, Mister Glassford, sir.' The heavy casement slipped from his grasp and closed with a clatter that made the glass shake.

John Glassford rounded on him crossly. 'Ye clumsy oaf,' he said, shaking his head. 'What do you think I keep you in green velvet and silver buckles for anyway? Smarten your ways, laddie, or by heaven, I swear you'll be sent to America with the rest of the trade.'

Walter looked at his toes sheepishly, saying nothing, and the crusty old merchant, seeing his discomfort, relented a little. 'Just don't forget your place, that's all,' he said more gently. 'If you don't, laddie, and it's a big "if" right now, I will maybe see to it that you get taught to read and write like I promised ye. But you have to smarten up your ways,' he added as a large grin spread across Walter's open, friendly face.

'Oh Mister Glassford,' Walter replied. 'Thank you, thank you sir.'

'Aye. Well. One "thank you" is enough lad,' Glassford answered gruffly. 'Fill me a pipe would you, and light it.'

Opening a small leather satchel, Walter took out the tobacco merchant's smoking things. A long wooden box monogrammed 'JG' revealed a number of slim churchwarden clay pipes, each one with a different design on the bowl. Walter filled Glassford's favourite pipe with well-rubbed Virginia leaf, and striking flint from a Japanned tinder-box, drew steadily until the tobacco was well alight. 'It's drawing now, Mr. Glassford,' he said, handing the pipe to his master.

'Thanks lad,' Glassford replied, puffing happily at the

curved white pipe.' 'Right,' he said after a minute's satisfaction. 'I'll see whoever there is now, Walter.'

Walter hurried across to open the door. 'Mister Ritchie?' he said, sticking his head out into the corridor.

James Ritchie strode into the room and held out his hand expansively. 'John!' he said, smiling. 'Good to see you.'

'That's fine, that's fine,' replied Glassford non-committally. 'Just wait outside a minute, Walter.'

The door closed quietly. James Ritchie stood in front of John Glassford, slightly at a loss. He coughed hollowly.

'Do you have the papers?' Glassford asked him sharply.

'Oh, the papers. Yes,' replied Ritchie, startled. He coughed again as he handed over a bundle of documents.

Glassford leafed through them silently.

'They're all there,' said James Ritchie.

'I would hope so,' Glassford said without looking up.

The minutes passed while Glassford read and his visitor coughed intermittently. After a little while the great merchant looked up. 'Seems to be all here,' he said. 'I've nine partners to consider, and three, as you know, canna speak for themselves richt now, being in Virginia.'

Ritchie leaned forward and pointed out a short list halfway down the top sheet. 'I have outlined the makeweight cargo,' he said, trying hard to suppress the dry rasp in his throat.

Glassford looked at him out of the corner of his eye.

'The brigantines *Betty* and *Martha*. Yes. I can see that. That's a bad cough you have there Ritchie,' he added as the man burst into a fit of spluttering and choking. 'Surprising for a man that works with the leaf all day,' he went on. 'Tobacco is good for your general health, cures the bowel flux, bad humours, and so on.'

'I know it does,' gagged the tobacco factor. 'I canna understand it at all. And I smoke as often as I can, too.'

45

MISS WALKINSHAW AND THE PALE
PRINCE

There was panic in the Council Chamber of the Town
House at Glasgow Cross. Over eight thousand wild
Highlanders, many barefoot, with Prince Charles Edward
Stuart, the Young Pretender, at their head, were marching
into Glasgow by the Back Cow Lone. Across the city
shutters were slamming and bolts shooting home as
screaming children were scooped out of the narrow streets
and courts by their terrified mothers, and those not actively
engaged in stuffing their valuables under the floorboards
were kneeling on them, praying. As the Highlanders
entered the town, legends followed these footsore, ragged
remnants of what had once been the proud army of a pale
and gaudy Prince. To some they were the agents of a
foreign and divisive power, to others, the last army of an
ancient and defeated kingdom; but even those who feared
the Highland army sensed the bitter pride that would carry
them to Culloden Moor.

The herald stood by Glasgow Cross, a curious and sullen
crowd listening as he made his proclamation. Charles
Edward Stuart and his captains sat still as statues, their
horses pawing the cobbles restlessly, the raw wind from the
east making the heavy embroidered standard flap and crack
like a whip.

The herald faced away from the wind so that his words
would carry further. '. . . and be it known,' he cried, 'that
his Noble Grace Charles Edward Stuart, Prince of the
Realm, be Regent in Absentia for his father, James that is
the Eighth of Scotland, King by the Grace of God of
England, Scotland, and Ireland, Fideat Defensor, Warden
of the Cinque Ports, here proclaimed in Glasgow at the
Merket Cross this twenty-ninth day of December in the

Year of Our Lord One Thousand Seven Hundred and Forty-five. Let all men hearken and obey.'

Bailie Cameron was not impressed. He turned to his friend, Bailie Jimmy Coates. 'Look at the fop sitting there,' he said. 'I never knew he had such dark hair.'

Jimmy Coates blew on his hands and rubbed them together. 'A French bawd wouldna' be seen in that jacket,' he said mournfully. 'Anyway,' he continued. 'That's not his hair. It's a wig.'

Cameron laughed. 'You mean a "Whig" daint ye?' he chortled. 'But that great Jacobite's nae Whig. And that thing on his head is real, man. And another thing, with that pale face with the freckles standing out he looks mair like a gypsy than anything.'

'Not forgetting the purple breeks,' added his friend.

'Don't speak to me about "breeks",' Jim Coates replied angrily. 'You know as well as I do that we've had to hand over six thousand tartan trews and twelve thousand linen shirts. God, man,' he spat in disgust. 'I'm beggared.'

'You're not the only one,' Cameron said, hiding his mouth with his hand. 'Did ye see Provost Cochrane's face when he said "I do this with great reluctance." Man, he was speaking from the heart.'

'But what can we do with all these wild Highlanders in Glasgow?' Bailie Coates asked.

'Ach, coats – if you'll pardon me saying so, Bailie Coates – coats and shoes willna' buy the rebels victory. They'll not be here for ever. If we bide our time they will be on their way again, you mark my words.'

'Then let's pray,' said his friend seriously, 'that we are both still here to see it when they do.'

The crowd milled about outside the Shawfield Mansion, hoping to catch a glimpse of Glasgow's famous uninvited guest. As soon as word had got about that the Prince intended to dine in the garden so that the people could see him, the curious, the idle, the hostile, and a handful of would-be supporters had walked down the Trongate to see if they could really see a scion of the House of Stuart at dinner. Sure enough, there he was, and with him, his only conquest in the city so far, Miss Clementina Walkinshaw. In spite of the drizzle, Charles Edward Stuart sat at table beneath a cloth awning. He was sharing a meal of cold chicken with his mistress, and returning the gaze of the crowd with something between indifference and hostility.

Clementina Walkinshaw cast a sidelong glance at the people gawping at them. 'People do stare, Charles,' she said, popping a marzipan sweetmeat into her full mouth.

'But that's why we are here, cheri, my dearest one,' Charles replied in heavily accented English. 'I am sorry if you are cold,' he went on, 'but there is the canopy, and you have your fur cape.' He nodded regally to the unresponsive mob of Glaswegians. 'We must look like a King for them,' he said out of the corner of his mouth.

Clementina fluttered her eyelashes at the Young Pretender. 'Glasgow is yours, my love,' she simpered.

Prince Charles Edward Stuart was not so sure. 'The people do not seem so very friendly,' he murmured, reaching for some roast ptarmigan. 'The quail's eggs are so small,' he complained.

Someone at the back of the crowd waved excitedly.

'Ah, friends,' said Charles. 'That is nice.'

'It would be if it was a nice gesture,' Clementina muttered quietly, but Charles heard her.

'Was he making signs not nice?' he asked, growing angry and forgetting his limited command of English. 'We cannot forget that Glasgow fortified itself against our cause fifteen years ago,' he went on. 'We do not trust these Glasgow burghers. I feel in my marrow that they would betray Us and Our gallant Highlanders, and all for a few sous.'

'That's not so my love,' his mistress assured him anxiously, patting his arm with her free hand, the other reaching for a dish of duck pâté. 'The people respect you,' she went on. 'You are a Prince, my Prince.'

'A Prince who will still be King,' he replied haughtily.

'Of course you will dearest,' Clementina said, stroking his chin with the tips of her fingers.

'If only I dared believe you, my pretty lady,' Charles

smiled. 'There were precious few of your townsmen joined me after my review on Glasgow Green.'

'But it was a glittering day,' she protested, 'and you the jewel in it.'

He looked at her, narrowing his eyes. 'Do you really think so?' he asked doubtfully.

'I know so, sire,' she replied. 'Do you remember the hawthorn tree you stood under to review your troops? The citizens of Glasgow already have a name for it.'

'And what is that?' said Charles warily.

'Why, your pardon, dearest, but they call it "Prince Charlie's Tree",' she giggled.

Charles looked at the people poking their noses through the railings in front of the house. 'Perhaps they are just excitable,' he said, standing up and nodding self-consciously to the crowd.

'Gang back tae France,' yelled a voice at the back of the crowd.

Charles turned to his mistress and frowned. 'What did he say, dearest?' he asked. 'You know the Glasgow speech.'

'He ... he said "Hail to the Prince",' she replied nervously, pouring herself a glass of wine.

Provost Cochrane looked over his shoulder to see if he was being watched, but the street was empty. He knocked on the door, then knocked again, and waited. After what seemed like a long time the door opened. In more normal times a servant would have stood there, ushering him in politely, but these were not normal times, and the master of the house himself, Bailie Cameron, stood there. 'Good morning Provost Cochrane,' he said without enthusiasm.

'What's good about it?' the Provost asked bleakly, walking into the hallway as Cameron, glancing outside before he did so, closed the door with a hollow boom.

When the Provost entered the study, he saw that most of the bailies and magistrates of Glasgow had preceded him. Seated or standing, the worthies of Glasgow looked as if they had lost a shilling and found the proverbial bawbee. In fact, they had already lost a great deal more.

Matthew Williamson thumped his fist on the table and demanded, 'Well? What's to be done? Will we just watch and applaud while the man ruins us?'

Interrupting the murmurs of agreement that greeted his outburst, Provost Cochrane said, 'We must do something about the rascal, that's plain, and the woman Walkinshaw is no better than he is.'

'He's a villain and a foreign bastard,' roared Cameron, 'and no daughter of mine would consort with him.'

'She no doubt thinks she is his consort,' answered the Provost.

'Cleverness is no' the way,' blurted Cameron, 'at least, no' cleverness with words. We will all be ruined by this madman yit! The hale toon hates his arrogant, starving rabble. Have ye seen them in our jackets, and our trews. Why, they look like, like . . . sacks of neeps with coats on.'

The Provost nodded. 'At least we can be thankful that only sixty joined him after his "great review" on the Green,' he said. 'And Himself was for letting your "neeps" loose on the town, Cameron, to do their will. You know what that would have meant!'

'Aye,' said Cameron. 'To loot and rape with our trousers on.'

Provost Cochrane put his hand on Cameron's shoulder. 'Calm yourself, man,' he said. 'The Cameron of Lochiel has dissuaded him. But look at us here, panicked like bees in a byke, you, Matthew Bogle, Gordon Surgoner, Providence McEnroy, Jamie Lundy. You know what it says in the Bible. "And Moses was sick and the lot fell on Aaron." We have but to bide our time. We have persuaded his man to accept £5,000 cash, not the £15,000 he demanded. The Highlanders have been kept from ruining us all, and we can make new jackets and shirts. Whether he goes back to Holyrood or stays here or whatever, mark my words, Gentlemen, it will be a week of months before Prince Charles, or any other Prince Charles, comes back to Glasgow.'

JAMES WATT INVENTS THE FUTURE

Long ago when the world was wider and greener, and industry was still predominantly an old woman at a loom in the kitchen, the machines of Glasgow were driven, pulled, pushed and lifted by basic old-fashioned horsepower – the variety that eats oats and needs a good rub down in the morning – or by human sweat and muscle. Dartmouth ironmonger Thomas Newcomen had first pumped water from a mine with his huge vertical steam engine in 1712, but since that time there had been little improvement in the gigantic engines that rose and fell like prehistoric insects, bristling with cast-iron flanges, bolts and ornate decorations. A steam engine of sorts had been puffing and hissing away as Bonnie Prince Charlie marched down the Trongate, but there was a long way to go before the inefficient mechanical monsters could be of more general use. The world needed a new source of power, but more than that, it needed the man who would have the genius to make it possible.

It was an early afternoon in 1764 and the calm of an eighteenth-century Sunday settled on the arches and the studies of the Old College. James Watt had left the College after Church and walking briskly towards the Clyde had entered Glasgow Green by a small wicket gate, the main gate being shut in case 'the wanton lieges should enjoy themselves on the Sabbath'. He strolled along, making for the Low Green and enjoying a quiet pipe and a good think. Walking in the park on a Sunday meant the risk of being caught by the 'Sabbath Men' and the possibility of a night in the cells or a heavy fine, but he thought the peace and quiet was worth it, and he had something more arresting on his mind than prison as he half-walked, half-ran back to the

51

College later that afternoon. The flagstones echoed as he ran across the quadrangle, under the Gothic arches of the old University building, and pounded up the ancient staircase to the workshop where he earned his living as a maker of 'philosophical instruments'.

He threw open the door and rushed eagerly into the room, muttering to himself as he rummaged about in the box of gears and springs on the bench. 'Now where in heaven's name is it?'

'Is . . . is that you, Mr. Watt?' said a rather fearful voice from the room next door.

'Aye, Sandy,' he replied. 'I'm back. Have you seen the large span dividers anywhere?'

'They're in the box, Mr. Watt,' said the thin voice.

James Watt looked again and, with a grunt of satisfaction, picked the needle-sharp instrument out from among a host of wires and cogs and threaded brass tubing as his sleepy assistant stumbled through to see what all the excitement was about.

'Ye gave me quite a fleg, Mr. Watt,' Sandy said, rubbing the sleep out of his eyes. 'Did ye forget something?'

James laughed. 'I'm sorry if I gave you a fright, son,' he smiled. 'It's not so much that I forgot something, rather that I've remembered an idea that's been hiding away at the back of my mind ever since Wednesday last when we got the College Newcomen in to be repaired.'

'D'ye mean the model steam engine, sir?' the apprentice replied drowsily. 'Ye didna forget it at all! It's finished, but ye weren't satisfied with the steam consumption or somethin'. Mind! Ye started to take it apart again.'

James took him by the shoulder and turned him gently towards the drawings of the broken engine spread out on the table under the window. 'See those drawings, lad,' he said. 'Well, they have started me on a different tack altogether. I think, only think, mind, that the answer is to build an expansion steam engine. You are right, you see. As it is now it uses up far too much steam. The answer is to build a separate condenser.'

He looked expectantly at the boy, but Sandy only

blinked. 'I'm not really with ye, Mr. Watt,' he stammered. 'What is a . . . separate condenser?'

James reached past him for the pad on the bench and began to draw rapidly. 'Look Sandy,' he said patiently. 'Here is the outside valve. Now, the thing is, the cylinder here should always be as hot as the steam which enters it there. Now if we close the top of the cylinder, then we can use low-pressure steam instead of cold air. It will probably take a year to prove it, but I imagine the temperature of the steam should be about 100°F or lower. We need a better boiler, too. The steam boilers we have been using are no better than copperies out of a whisky still, but the key will probably be to condense the steam in a separate closed vessel instead of the cylinder itself.'

Sandy wrinkled his forehead as he studied the careful drawing on the table. 'I'm sorry, Mr. Watt. I still don't understand what ye mean,' he said.

'Well, look,' said the man on the brink of paving the way to the Industrial Revolution. 'Sit down, laddie, and I'll explain a bit more slowly. You see, that helps me as well. The first thing is to look at the density and pressure of steam.'

Sandy's stomach grumbled pathetically.

'Is that you?' asked James Watt. 'I'm sorry, son. The idea of food had gone clean out of my mind. We can have a bite to eat and then have another look at the wee engine.'

The gold of the evening sunlight was just fading from the tops of the poplars along the road to Dumbarton as it wandered dustily into the village of Partick, when the door of the Anderston Club opened, admitting James Watt to the cheery noise, the crackling warmth of the log fire, and the smell of hot how-towdie and roasting chicken. Scattered groups of men sat about talking in low voices, eating or sipping their claret and squeezing fresh limes into their rum. He nodded to them as he went past, but James' goal was the figure seated with his back to him by the far door, and as he approached, the man, who had been dealing firmly with a plate of hot chicken broth, put down his spoon and turned. 'James!' he said heartily. 'Come away and sit down. Will I get you some towdie?'

'No, thanks,' James replied. 'But I'll share some talk with you, Joseph, if you don't mind.'

Professor Joseph Black looked at the man sitting across the table from him, his grey bushy eyebrows hiding the twinkle in his eye. 'I got your note, James,' he said. 'What are you so all-fired excited about? Have you discovered the secret of perpetual motion?'

'No, Joseph,' James answered quickly. 'It's the changes I am making to the model steam engine.'

'Changes? What changes?' asked the old Professor.

James Watt sat silently for a moment. When he spoke, it was nervously, as if unsure of himself. 'You see Joseph,' he said, 'I think I'm going to need some suport for the new idea I have. You know as well as anyone that it's not always been easy for me. I didn't come the usual road, not being in the Guild and so on.'

Professor Black smiled quietly. 'I know James,' he said, 'but the only man in this room unaware of what James Watt can do is James Watt. So you never completed your term as an apprentice, and now it's all being put on you, even the talk of a survey for the Clyde Canal. People judge you by what you do, James. Never mind anything else.'

'I suppose you're right,' James replied doubtfully, 'and I know you are a good friend, Joseph, but I want to put forward my discovery in the best possible light.'

Professor Black eyed him carefully. 'Just what is this discovery of yours? Is it optics?'

'Not at all,' James replied excitedly. 'Nothing to do with that.' He paused. 'It's ... steam!' James said self-consciously, lowering his voice.

'You are the jester, James,' said the Professor. 'I thought for a minute there you said "steam".'

'I did.' James answered, his face a mask of seriousness. The Professor looked uncomfortable.

'Listen to me Joseph,' James urged him. 'I was out for my usual Sunday walk on Glasgow Green, keeping a wary eye out for the Sabbath Men and thinking about this and that, but mainly about the steam engine.'

'You mean the Newcomen?' Black asked him.

'Well, yes and no,' James continued. 'I'd gone about as far as the goat-herd's house and my head was a perfect vacuum, when it came to me all in a rush, about the vacuum I mean.'

Professor Black squared his shoulders and leaned against the wooden partition. 'James,' he said slowly. 'Are you suggesting that you can give the engine more power?'

'That's it, Joseph! Exactly,' James replied excitedly. 'I think it is possible to build a steam engine small enough and powerful enough to drive . . . oh anything, looms, farming machines, perhaps even, even ships!'

The Professor smiled indulgently at his friend's earnestness. 'Ships!' he said, with a note of incredulity creeping into his voice. 'Why James, even if, and I do say "if", ships could be propelled by your new steam engine, it is a well-known fact, man, that flesh and blood cannot survive at speeds greater than thirty miles an hour!'

'I don't know about that, Joseph,' James answered with animation, 'but I worked it all out on the Green. I'll maybe need to take out a patent on it. What I'm saying, Joseph, is that I can build a new engine that could even be put to driving a carriage. Why, one day the streets of Glasgow might be full of carts and phaetons and gigs all driven by the power of steam, not by horses. Think of it! Carriages with engines, ships with engines. Why, steam will turn the wheels of the world!'

Professor Black sat silently for what seemed like a long time. At last James Watt could stand it no longer. 'Well?' he demanded. 'What do you think, friend Professor?'

'I think . . . I think you must be practical,' Joseph Black replied. 'Looms, agriculture, all that I can see, but no horses? Now you are dreaming, James Watt.'

BROTHERS UNDER THE SKIN

The formal study of medicine didn't begin in Glasgow until the 1700s, but even after that time the town was bursting with unqualified practitioners, quacks, mountebanks and tooth-pulling conjurors. Common preparations offered to the suffering citizenry included such choice items as powder of Egyptian mummy, goose-fat dressing for boils, jellied cobwebs, curative syllabubs, vegetable cocktails, and a variety of balsams and ointments made from ingredients that even the charlatans of the day hesitated to describe.

It was into this world of amateur medicine and surgeon-barbers that two brothers came from Long Calderwood in East Kilbride. William and John Hunter were to become, in their different ways, the twin fathers of modern scientific surgery, anatomy, and obstetrics.

William's training was more formal and academic than that of his brother John. He studied at Glasgow University, but eventually turned his hopes and his career in the direction of London. He was the polished gentleman of the pair, and he bought a house in Great Windmill Street in London, rebuilding it to contain a lecture theatre, dissecting rooms and a museum, but as his reputation as a teacher and anatomist grew he turned increasingly to obstetrics. Among his many rich and famous patients he numbered Queen Charlotte, to whom he became the first male widwife. His discoveries and his brilliance were summed up in his giant folio *The Anatomy of the Gravid Uterus, Illustrated in Figures*, which was lovingly engraved by the faithful and sympathetic Dutchman, Jan van Rymsdyck.

If William was a diamond among doctors, then brother John remained a largely uncut gem, at least in manners. He never completed a course of study at the University, and, like most surgeons of his day, never attempted to become a qualified medical doctor. At first, after following his brother to London, he helped him prepare dissections for his anatomy lectures, but after studying at a number of London hospitals, he entered St. Mary's Hall, Oxford, as a gentleman commoner. After two months John could stand the dry and dusty academic life no longer, and he left. He loved nature, not the library, and for him there was no book like the human body. Later, like his brother William, he taught widely, and also like his brother, gained a fame that led to honours and wealth. He was acknowledged as the leading surgeon in London and even became Surgeon Extraordinary to George III as well as Surgeon General and Inspector General of Hospitals. His burning passion was to know and to learn from his own experiments.

Eventually, the brilliant brothers fell out, but for many years they would still occasionally travel together, even returning to their favourite haunts in Glasgow, like the shop with the bow windows of bull's-eye glass and its stock of undiscovered treasures – Smollet's the Bookshop in the High Street of the Old Town. In the year 1769, when grocers advertised their tea as 'genuine and not adulterated with sawdust like some', when Queen's Dock was a grazing ground for carriage horses and pigs went for five shillings and brandy was tuppence a glass, they found themselves at Smollet's once again.

William Hunter pinched his upper lip and turned away from the pile of books and manuscripts in the corner. Explosively, annoyingly, a sneeze was rising at the back of his nose. 'Ahh . . . choo!' he exploded.

His brother laughed.

Ignoring him, William smoothed his collar and straightened his wig with careful dignity. 'The dust on these books!' he exclaimed. 'I'm sure these manuscripts have not seen a lick of a cloth since last we were here, John. Much as I love the printed word, 'tis plaguey vexatious. Look! It gets thicker while you watch it, I swear!'

John Hunter laughed again, a rich, earthy laugh founded

in his practical and honest nature. 'Ah, but you are the gentleman, brother mine,' he said. 'I would have thought that all that powder from the wigs in London would have made your nose the master of such things.'

'Indeed, sirrah,' replied his brother sternly. 'Those selfsame "wigs", and their wives, have been bread and butter to both of us. Am I not Queen Charlotte's midwife? That is not to be sneezed at!'

'When you are being serious,' said John Hunter with a twinkle in his eye, 'you are at your best. But listen, the real story isna here.'

'What d'ye mean?' asked his brother absently as he peered at the title of a faded volume lying on the deep windowsill. 'What isn't here?' he asked again.

'The truth,' answered John earnestly. 'What about Aristotle and the fish?'

'To the devil with Aristotle,' said William, straightening up and looking at John in a superior way. 'What's he got to do with anything?'

'Experiment!' John replied, the light of battle kindling in his eye. 'Aristotle gave his students the task of describing the structure of a fish. Some of the students went away and came back several days later with beautiful and elegant essays about their fish, which by this time stank to high heaven, but others, William,' and he poked his brother in the waistcoat for emphasis, 'others never went away at all to look up references and learned treatises. Ye know what they did?'

'No,' said William distantly, 'but I think I'm going to.'

Ignoring the sarcasm, John continued. 'They dissected and anatomized the thing. Instead of blindly copying the errors and imaginings of "scholars" who had, like as not, imitated others before them, a few did what the great man hoped and observed for themselves.'

William looked at his brother and coughed politely. 'And did Aristotle himself tell you this, John?'

'What? What d'ye mean, William? Of course not, I read it in a . . .' and he started to laugh. 'You damned rascal,' he began. 'You had that in your mind all the time.'

'It's logic,' said his brother with a wave of his hand as he turned to go. 'Reason. And if you want that book in your hand, John Hunter, you had better "reason" some gold out of your pocket.'

John Hunter looked down at the book as if it had suddenly appeared by magic. 'Now where did this come from?' he said in mock-surprise. 'I don't remember picking this up!'

'Aye, well,' replied his brother with a sigh. 'If you want it I suggest you pay for it. This time you settle the bill and I'll fumble, but perhaps you would rather have gone to the fish shop.' And William Hunter ran round the corner of a large bookcase before anything heavier than words could be hurled after him.

Later that evening, John and William Hunter were sitting in their rooms, talking and arguing. The decanter of claret was well on the way to changing colour from a rich dark ruby to the twinkling clarity of emptiness, and John Hunter was doing everything he could to hasten the process along.

'Dain't you think that's rather enough,' said William. 'We have an early rise for the coach tomorrow, John.'

'Don't be so high and sanctimonious, midwife!' said John, sitting down heavily across the table from his brother. 'I know what's good for me. I prescribe a little more of . . . this!' And he drained the lees of the decanter into his tall glass. 'Edinburgh, ye know,' he said speculatively. 'That's Edinburgh glass, that is. See the twisted spirals up inside the stem. Good glass that is, I know.'

'I know you do, John,' said his brother soothingly. 'But, John,' he pleaded, 'I'm only thinking of you.'

'Oh I know ye are,' answered John. 'You think I have no culture, no manners. When we get back to London, brother, come to Earl's Court and I'll show you my bees, leopards, blackbirds, hedgehogs, and the way to experiment with the lower animals.'

'It's the experiment with another animal that worries me,' replied his brother, deftly sliding John's glass across the table out of his reach. 'It's the experiments you are conducting on yourself, John. Are you any closer to a cure?'

John looked across at him with eyes slightly befuddled but full of a deep well of intelligence. 'You know I infected myself with the Lesser Pox, William?' he said quietly.

'I do, John. Have you been using the mercury?'

'Mercury!' John sneered. 'That's the way to make your teeth and hair fall out. Listen, William. I have kept careful records of every substance I have used and one of them proved effective.'

'But that's great news, man,' said his brother with relief. 'How wonderful for ye.'

'Aye, well, maybe not,' John said doubtfully. 'Ye see, Will, when it started to clear up and I wisny sure what exactly was dealing with the disease, I decided to re-infect myself and start all over again.'

'*What?*' said William in amazement. 'Ye've *what*, John?'

'Gied masel' it again,' John answered, slurring his words slightly. 'But this time . . . I'm afraid it's the Great Pox, and I'll never cure that.'

There was a silence. 'Then you have taught me something tonight,' said William solemnly.

'What's that?' John asked sleepily.

'That the word "never" is a part of your vocabulary,' his brother answered with quiet respect.

'Aye, maybe,' laughed John, 'but I'll tell ye this Will, never again!'

THE BARD AT THE BLACK BULL

The year 1787 had been marked by changeable weather. In the winter and spring high winds and torrential rain had caused the Clyde to become as full of flood water as a half-pint glass with a pint in it. By June, the cold had given way to a glorious summer and it seemed as though Glasgow had proved itself worthy of the title of the 'Florence of the North'. Now winter was back once again.

Robert Burns was as tempestuous as the weather had been earlier in the year. The erratic genius of this shooting star led him from love affair to love affair, but always, whether hiding from a writ, travelling or talking, the master word-smith of Scotland wrote and wrote and spent his gifts liberally for all the world.

In January, the Grand Lodge of Scotland had toasted him as 'Caledonia's Bard', but he had turned away from Edinburgh life for a while and toured the Borders and planned a journey through the West Highlands as far as Inveraray. Then he had ridden slowly along the south bank of the Clyde towards Glasgow, returning the following December for a second visit.

The Black Bull Inn stood at the corner of Argyle Street and Virginia Street. It was a fine sandstone building of three storeys with the sweep of a steep gable on top and rows of chimneys. Burns' room was to the left of the central portion and commanded a view down to the masts and sails of the ships at anchor on the river.

The rattle and chatter of the bustling streets outside paled before the steady 'tick, tick, tick . . .' of the clock on the mantel. As the mechanism chimed three slowly, Robert Burns went on limping backwards and forwards across the room like a ram in a wicker cage.

'That's three already, Robert,' said his friend John

Wilson. 'You've been in Glasgow a week now and you still canna settle.'

'It's fine for you to talk, John Wilson!' Burns replied heatedly. 'You are the teacher and session clerk here. No doubt for you the world is just where it should be all the time.'

'Not so!' protested his friend. 'You know me better than that, Robert.'

Burns immediately regretted his tone. 'I'm sorry for that, John,' he said, 'but how many days is it since I met Clarinda?'

'If this is December the ...'

'Ninth,' Robert Burns supplied helpfully.

'Aye, well, ninth then. Five days. December the fourth it was, and your arithmetic is as good as anyone's, Robert, except when it comes to the fair sex.'

'To "Clarinda",' Burns reminded him.

John Wilson frowned disapprovingly. 'The Mistress Agnes Maclehose,' he said with emphasis.

Burns turned towards the window. 'Would she were my Mis ...' he began, stopping short and wincing with pain. 'Damn my leg!' he said with feeling.

'Well you will pace up and down like a bear on heat,' John Wilson scolded. 'It's but two days since ye dislocated yer knee, man! Sit down for pity's sake, or you'll be the "Lame Bard of Caledonia". Permanently!'

Burns hobbled over to the table and balanced himself on the edge of a chair, the offending leg jutting out to one side. 'I feel like a peg-leg sailor,' he said. 'Who would have me like this?'

'More than one, and you know it, Robert,' his friend smiled. 'Now stop feeling sorry for yourself. Do you think you could manage to stumble out for a dram?'

'That's a wonder and a miracle,' Burns replied, beaming. 'This knee's as right as rainwater.' He attempted to rise, winced again, and sat down heavily.

'Do as you are told,' said John, shaking his head sympathetically. 'Keep yourself busy. Do you want to write?'

'Aye, I will, friend "Doctor",' Burns answered firmly.

'To Agnes Maclehose?' asked John.

'If it matters overmuch to you, John, it's not to her at all, it's to Annie.'

'Annie who?' his friend replied blankly. 'I don't remember that one.'

'Now behave yersel', John, will ye?' Burns said, gasping as he reached across the table for pen and ink. 'You remember Annie.'

'Oh,' sighed John Wilson, refusing to be drawn, 'that Annie.'

'Och you're being a right Holy Willie today,' Burns said, licking the tip of the pen and dipping it in the blue-grey ink.

The sound of Burns' pen scratching on the paper mingled with the ticking of the clock and the muted bustle from the street. John Wilson stood staring out of the window.

'What is it that you see in this Maclehose woman?' he asked at last.

'Lady, John, lady,' chided the poet. 'My eye is for the ladies, no' for women. John Wilson, you are a right Doctor Hornbrook and no mistake.'

'Who?' asked his friend.

'Oh,' Burns mused absently. 'Just somebody I have in mind.'

The seagulls wheeled in ever decreasing circles as the clipper emptied its bilges by the quay. A circle of men sweated at the windlass as chains rattled and clanked across the worn edges of the heavy wooden piers. Stepping daintily over a puddle, Miss Wilhelmina Alexander took Robert Burns' arm again as they left the sounds of labour and the sweating stevedores behind. The sun came out from behind a cloud, and for a moment the Clyde sparkled all the way down to Govan, but the sun vanished and the river was once again a gloomy, noisy, workaday waterway smelling of tar and oil and the growing city up the hill.

'You know, I'd forgotten all this since the summer,' Burns said. 'July to December. It's like the difference between Edinburgh and Glasgow, but there is a strength in the winter. In winter you have to fight.'

'And yet you brought me here, Robert,' the young woman said. 'What is so beautiful in all this?'

' "All this" is a great river, Mina darling. It's a port, and that means it's the world as well.'

'I had thought your mind was more on me than ships, Robert,' she said, holding his arm a little tighter.

'Of course, darling,' he replied, favouring her with a smile. 'But look at that beauty! I was thinking of going to the Indies in a brigantine like that, you know.'

'And where are you bound for now, Robert Burns?' she asked, sulking.

He turned and held her lightly by the shoulders. 'I'm bound for you, darling Mina,' he replied, kissing her lightly on the cheek. 'I want us to be together.'

'No you don't,' she said, turning her head away.

'Mina, look at me. That's it,' he smiled, turning her head gently towards him. He stroked her lips with his fingers.

Suddenly she broke away and took a step back. 'Robert!' she said firmly. 'Now listen to me.'

He reached forward and stroked her hair.

'No, I mean it,' she insisted, shaking her head. 'I don't want to share you. I can't bear to think of all these people sharing your thoughts and feelings. It's frightening.'

Burns stood up a little straighter and looked at her seriously. 'But that's my work,' he said. 'A man is what he does. My poems are the property of the world.'

'You are insufferable,' she said angrily. 'I don't want you to belong to the world. I want you to belong to me.'

'Oh, but I do,' he replied, putting his arms around her.

As they stood in the shadows, Burns and the Bonny Lass of Ballochmyle, ships sailed down the river to the world that already had a part of Wilhelmina Alexander.

Robert Burns and John Wilson strolled along the Gallowgate, the poet still suffering from a slight limp.

'As I was saying, John,' he said, 'who would understand a woman, eh?'

'It's your own fault, Robert. How many strings have you got to your bow? What about Agnes? What about Wilhelmina?'

'We are a good way east of the Black Bull now,' Robert answered, changing the subject.

'We are almost at the Saracen's Head Inn,' replied his friend. 'Johnson stayed here.'

'Ah,' laughed Burns knowingly. 'With his lap-dog Boswell. Johnson visited more inns than an exciseman. Shall we go in?'

'Why not?' said John Wilson. 'It is your last night in Glasgow.'

'Yes, regrettably,' Burns answered, 'but I have, er, someone to visit. I have a song in mind,' he added as they entered the smoke and clamour of the inn.

'Of course,' smiled John Wilson. 'If you could see yourself the way other people see you, Robert, you might, just might, realize that you are something of a great man for all that. Not that I want you to get big-headed.'

Robert Burns hummed softly to himself.

'What's that?' asked John Wilson.

'A tune, a poem,' said Burns. 'Something.' He sighed. 'Maybe it's Clarinda put it in my mind. Anyway, I started writing a song at the Black Bull before we came out, but it's not finished yet.'

'A good one?' asked John with an understanding born of friendship.

'Could be,' said Robert Burns. 'I call it "Ae Fond Kiss".'

People milled about, shuffling through the sawdust on the floor, and shouted or drank noisily.

'Do you want to go back?' asked John Wilson, raising his voice.

'No.' Burns shouted. 'We might as well have one now. I was just thinking about dark hair. Do you like dark hair, John?'

'Robert Burns,' John roared with laughter. 'I give you up entirely . . . to the lassies.'

THE CANDLELIT NIGHT SCHOOL

Europe was in turmoil and the name 'Napoleon' featured constantly in the Glasgow press, the *Herald and Advertiser*, the *Glasgow Journal* and the *Courier*. The new century would see the dawn of vast industries enriched by the coalfields of central Scotland and Ayrshire and the beginnings of a brilliant tradition of engineering. Ships were to rumble down the slipways by the hundred, railways would spread their steel fingers across the land, spanning rivers and fields, mountains and gorges, but at the start of the nineteenth century, the foundations of that great workshop of the British Empire were being laid in Glasgow.

The city had become a magnet and a mecca for industry, and the need and the desire for education in the sciences and engineering was being met by the Andersonian Institution, named after its benefactor Dr. John Anderson, Professor of Natural Philosophy at Glasgow University.

John Anderson was a 'man o' pairts' in his own right, and had helped defend Stirling Castle against Bonnie Prince Charlie's army in 1745. The government showed little interest in his theories about electricity and gunnery, so he demonstrated them to the French army. His travelling companion was the swashbuckling sea-captain and privateer John Paul Jones, hero of the American Revolution. Anderson's special interest was 'the training of skilled artisans and mechanics'. His Institution was well equipped with working models, and the library of scientific and technical books in several languages was being added to all the time. By 1800 the 'candlelit night school' was well on the way to becoming a permanent feature of Glasgow life.

Dr. Birbeck leaned forward and peered over Mr. Orne's shoulder. 'It's important you get it working well,' he said to his mechanic anxiously. 'It duplicates the action of the Boulton and Watt engines going into the textile mills.'

'I'm doing my best, sir,' replied Mr. Orne.

The little machine on the table began to hiss and bubble, and the brass piston gleamed and became a blur as the eccentric motion gathered speed. There was an ominous deep-throated 'hiss' from the miniature boiler, and suddenly a needle of white-hot steam shot out towards the two men.

'It's richt lucky you weren't standing closer, Dr. Birbeck,' Orne said solicitously.

Birbeck looked down at the sodden pagodas and peacocks on his waistcoat. 'Well,' he said sarcastically. 'It's only the finest African silk, Mr. Orne. But we can't have these models bursting around us like bubbles. What's the cause of it, man?'

Mr. Orne started poking and tapping the little engine with his spanner, flustered that the precious toy had refused to behave itself. 'It's not the condenser,' he muttered, going down on his knees and reaching behind the boiler. 'The wee valve's intact. These things are fiddly, Dr. Birbeck, not like the real machines at all!' He stood up suddenly and said triumphantly: 'There we are! The centrifugal governor is loose and willna' regulate the speed and size of the valve here . . . so it disna dae the job there . . . See?'

'Not entirely,' Dr. Birbeck replied. 'Will the machine need to be replaced?'

'No, no, bless you sir,' Mr. Orne grinned genially. 'Not a bit of it. I'll have this wee thing running as smooth as your African silk by the evening.'

The doctor sighed. 'One can but hope, I suppose. Dr. Garnet assured me that everything here would stand up well to the rigours of the classroom. This steamer is essential to this evening's demonstration.'

'I'll do what I can,' smiled the mechanic.

Birbeck looked at him with a jaundiced eye. 'Please see

that you do.' And he left the room, brushing the front of his waistcoat with his hands.

The audience in the lecture theatre were growing restless. Candlelight from the iron chandeliers made shadows dance on the wall, expanding hats and heads and hair into flickering mountains on the plaster ceiling.

Dr. Birbeck stood, trying not to look at the restless crowd or listen to the metal heartbeat of the turnip watch thumping and ticking in his pocket. He was just about to make a 'final' announcement when the door behind the rostrum opened and Mr. Orne backed onto the stage, staggering slightly under the small but solid weight of the model Boulton and Watt. 'Here she is, Doctor! Repaired and polished!' he said, setting the engine on the table heavily and making the test tubes and retorts rattle.

Sounds of amusement came from the audience and Dr. Birbeck glowered. 'Ah . . . good man!' he announced in a loud, theatrical manner, adding in a whisper, 'I was just about to give them the transparent seagull's skull.'

'Oh aye?' Orne replied, wiping machine oil from his fingers with a crumpled floral rag that he produced from his trouser pocket. 'How was that made like that?' he asked blandly.

'An interesting experiment in chemistry,' Birbeck answered with impatience, 'but some other time, man.' He looked at the steam engine. 'Does it work?' he whispered.

'Does it work?' replied Orne, offended. 'Does it . . .? Of course it does.'

'Well, get it going then,' snapped Birbeck.

Orne reached for a spill and thrust it into a candle. The coloured wood sputtered into flame and in a moment was transferred deftly to the wick beneath the model boiler. The piston began to slide smoothly back and forward as the wheels gathered speed and the repaired governor rose like a little expanding triangle above the whirring machine.

'There you are,' Orne said with satisfaction. 'Smooth as a bairn's . . .'

'Excellent, excellent,' Dr. Birbeck interrupted him

hastily. 'That will be everything, thank you, Orne.'

'I'll be up at the back of the room if you want me. Don't mind if I have a wee listen do you?'

'No, not at all,' replied Dr. Birbeck impatiently. 'If you can find room. If you want to learn you are welcome Mr. Orne, but right up at the back if you please.'

Dr. Birbeck walked to the front of the rostrum and cleared his throat. The audience looked at him expectantly. 'Good evening, gentlemen, and ladies,' he began, 'I am sorry about the, er, slight delay. Wheels within wheels, you know.'

The audience looked at him stonily.

Reddening, he launched into his lecture. 'This evening I will look at the engines used in modern chemistry. To begin with, the chemistry of fixed air or carbon dioxide, as used in the dyeing process ...' He continued, punctuating his lecture with experiments, and soon every member of his audience was watching in fascination.

Some time later, he put down his chalk and strode away from the blackboard. 'In conclusion,' he said, 'a dram of pure salt of tartar will dissolve in fourteen pounds of limewater. Now, are there any questions?'

People looked at each other, wondering who would be first to speak out. 'Come now,' he said encouragingly. 'There must be someone with a question!'

Towards the back of the hall a hand appeared above the sea of faces.

'Could you stand up, sir?' asked Dr. Birbeck loudly.

A young man in working clothes got reluctantly to his feet. 'Sir, I'm a mechanic,' he began. 'I don't know if this chemistry you're talking about will help me better myself at the machines. I've walked here to Glasgow from Paisley, and I had hoped to be given some more understanding of my work with hope of advancement.'

'Why, yes, I would hope you will, Mr. . . .?' asked Dr. Birbeck.

'Mackie, Ian Mackie,' replied the mechanic.

'Well, Mr. Mackie,' the lecturer said earnestly. 'The aim and reason for the Andersonian Institution is to help people like yourself, but we hope to cover everything to do with general physics, not just one area alone.'

'But chemistry's not a great deal of use to me, Doctor,' the mechanic said.

Doctor Birbeck stepped forward to get a clearer view of his questioner. 'Is there steam then in your place of work?'

Ian Mackie took a step down towards the rostrum. 'There's been steam in our cotton factory since 1792,' he said. 'We have mair American cotton in Paisley than in America, sir.'

'I'm afraid I don't quite see your point.' Dr. Birbeck frowned.

'You will have to go slower,' the mechanic said candidly.

Dr. Birbeck nodded in approval. 'Then I will, sir. Mr. Anderson wrote a special textbook for mechanics and artisans like yourself and I will be delighted to show you a copy after the lecture.'

'Will I pay much for that?' Ian Mackie asked timidly.

Without answering, Dr. Birbeck walked behind the table, returning with a small cloth-bound book in his hand. He stepped down off the rostrum and climbed the stairs towards the mechanic. 'How many hours have you worked today?' he asked.

'Thirteen, sir,' replied the man.

Dr. Birbeck put the book in his hand. 'Any man that works thirteen hours and then walks thirteen miles to learn has paid already,' he said, walking back to the table where the little steam engine was still busily hissing and puffing its way towards tomorrow.

By 1828 the Andersonian Institution had become Anderson's University. By 1877 it was Anderson's College; by 1896, the Glasgow and West of Scotland Technical College; by 1912, the Royal Technical College, Glasgow; by 1956, the Royal College of Science and Technology. And in 1963 it became the University of Strathclyde.

DOON THE WATTER TO THE WORLD

In the early years of the nineteenth century, ships from the Clyde spread their net from the West Indies to the Baltic, from Spain to America, and a worldwide traffic in coal, coffee, worsteds, iron, flax, hemp and a thousand other items led fleets and flotillas to strange lands and far-off islands – but always with the trade winds at their backs. In the doldrums or becalmed, the fastest white-winged clipper was as helpless as a dugout in a backwater.

It was, however, an age of industry and enterprise. A new Iron Age had dawned and new machines were appearing every day. Henry Bell, a mason and millwright, had already thought of applying steam power to ships, and he and his engineer friend John Robertson were in the process of putting together a design for their *Comet*, the father of every great ship that in future years Clydeside would send down its slipways and out into the oceans. It was a small but significant beginning. Canvas and rigging would soon give way to smokestacks, paddle-wheels, propellers and turbines – and all because the *Comet*, the world's first commercial steamboat, puffed down the Clyde and into history.

The washing was strung across the back-court like flags from the masthead of a ship of the line. Down below, the wooden shed that occupied the space between the tenements periodically emitted a rosy glow. The air rang with bangs and crashes that would not have been out of place at the Battle of Trafalgar, seven years before.

John Pettigrew watched with growing impatience as his apprentice attempted to hammer an iron band down over the top of the metal cylinder between his knees. 'I said temper the band again, William,' he shouted over the noise.

'You're not shoeing a horse, laddie!'

William stopped and drew a deep breath, wiping the sweat from his forehead on a grimy cuff. 'Right Mr. Pettigrew, I'll give it another wee dip.' He eased the metal circle from the tube and carried it across to the furnace. After a moment he returned, the ring of metal now a bright shimmering red.

'That's not long enough,' Mr. Pettigrew said curtly.

'It was still very hot,' countered the apprentice, 'and I put it at the back of the coals. There's nae scale on it.'

'Well I'll scale you, my lad, if it bursts,' answered his master sternly. 'Temper it then, if you're going to.'

William plunged the fiery ring into a large bucket of salt water. A cloud of steam billowed up as he used the tongs to turn the metal over. Gingerly, he lifted the metal out. It was now a dense grey-black, but still very warm, and he placed the circle carefully over the top of the tube. It slipped down a little way then stopped. 'It's still a good fit, sir,' he said anxiously, tapping it at the side, 'and there's to be enough to be riveted as well.'

Mr. Pettigrew took a step back and squinted at the long iron tube lying in the shallow earth trench. 'Get on with it, then,' he nodded at William. 'Just you forge the iron, and I'll worry about riveting. Mr. Bell is verra clear about the dimensions of the funnel for his steamboat. Although I must say, if he'd asked me I would have said he might have been better off making it out of brick, even though I am the smith.' He looked on as William frantically swung his hammer. 'Is that it now?' he asked.

'Aye, sir,' William replied with satisfaction.

Mr. Pettigrew walked round to the other side of the tube. 'I think we'll manage it together,' he said at last with a frown. 'Give us a lift, boy!'

'It's still a bittie rough at the flanges,' William muttered doubtfully, running his finger along the top edge.

'What have I taught ye?' said his employer, handing him a large file. 'Use the rasp, boy. There – and there and all.'

With a grinding sound the file began to pare away the metal flash and Mr. Pettigrew bent down to turn the cylinder as William worked his way around it.

They were interrupted by a voice behind them. 'Good day, Mr. Pettigrew,' said Henry Bell, taking off his top hat and mopping his forehead with a linen handkerchief. 'Hot as Hades in here, eh?'

'Aye, that's just it,' answered the smith, standing up and rubbing his fingers against the sides of his leather apron. 'There she is, Mr. Bell.' He pointed to the long cylinder on the ground. Henry Bell nodded. 'What about your boiler, though, Mr. Bell?' Pettigrew asked his client.

'Boiler and engine are well in hand with Mr. Napier and Mr. Robertson, John,' Bell replied. 'I would have been over here sooner, but there were some papers to see to, for registering her you understand. I seem to have been on my feet for days, looking to this, overseeing that . . .'

'Och, I know you are a busy man,' Mr. Pettigrew said solicitously. 'Registering, you say?'

'Why do you have to register your ship, Mr. Bell?' asked William, putting down his hammer.

'Now, William,' his master rounded on him. 'Just you mind your place. Mr. Bell has better things to do than explain these matters to an apprentice.'

'When it comes to steamships we are all apprentices,' laughed Henry Bell. 'The lad's just curious.'

'If you say so,' replied Mr. Pettigrew, shocked. An apprentice questioning a client was an event almost as revolutionary for him as the idea of a ship driven by steam.

Henry Bell took several large sheets of paper out of the pocket of his topcoat. 'The first thing, lad,' he said grandly, 'is the advertisement. I was at the offices of the *Chronicle* this morning, and placed a notice about the new ship and its services. See here,' he said. ' "The elegance, safety, comfort and speed of this vessel require only to be seen to meet the approbation of the public, and the proprietor is determined to do everything in his power to merit general support" – and more of the same to encourage people to take an interest in the new principle. But that's not registering her. That needs a careful description.' He extracted another piece of paper from his pocket and unfolded it carefully. ' "The *Comet*",' he said, reading again. ' "A square-stemmed caravel, full-built passage boat with a cockpit to carry forty passengers, forty feet long, twelve feet broad, and to draw four feet of water." ' He paused. 'And here, here is the real matter of it, lad,' he added with pride. ' "Being furnished with a steam engine, by which she sails." '

William listened with wide eyes. 'It takes a lot of words to launch a ship,' he said at last. 'But why does it need the big chimney like we've been makin' for ye, Mr. Bell?'

'Mr. Bell is doing his best to explain it to you, William,' said his master with a note of menace in his voice.

'Och, it's natural John, natural,' Henry Bell replied, but he ignored William's question. 'Is that it ready though?' he asked Pettigrew, nodding at the funnel.

'Oh aye,' said the master smith, glad to change the subject. 'But I'm in two minds whether to take it down the close at number 9 Sauchiehall Street, or along the pend into Buchanan Street. The close is a wee bit on the narrow side.'

'I would say the way I came in,' Henry Bell answered thoughtfully. 'Two six one Buchanan Street, John. Would you not agree?'

'If you wish, sir,' said Mr. Pettigrew, 'but it's uphill.'

'Well what do you suggest?' said Bell with the impatience of a man exhausted by the pursuit of a dream.

'Best thing's along Sauchiehall Street,' said the smith.

'I would say so too, sir,' interrupted William.

'When we want your opinion, we'll ask for it,' said John Pettigrew, raising his eyebrows.

William busied himself with a non-existent speck of rust on the funnel, and Henry Bell continued. 'If you could manage the windings of the close that would be better,' he said. 'The carter will be along that way first, and I'm anxious the *Comet*'s funnel should not get stuck up a close, or the future of steam power in ships might be set back a generation.'

John Pettigrew saw the twinkle in Bell's eye, and they both began to laugh together. 'Na, na, that'll no' happen, sir,' he said. 'We can manage her for ye, eh William?'

William nodded vigorously.

'Right then, let's lift her!' ordered the smith. 'Easy now, lad. Down your end a bit.'

Followed by an anxious Henry Bell, the smokestack of the world's first commercial steamship scraped and edged its way along a Glasgow close.

Seagulls screamed and mewled over the churning wake of the *Comet* as she headed downstream, midway between Glasgow and Greenock. A mixed party of guests and passengers sat or stood gingerly, holding on to the side-rails, as the flat blades of the paddles dug deep into the chilly waters of the Clyde. The adventurous crew of four, master and pilot, engineer and fireman, laboured to keep the ship in steam and on course, but Henry Bell was intent on other matters.

'And so you can see, gentlemen,' he said loudly, 'there is no danger, either in our four paddles working constantly or the tremendous speed we have attained. It was the comet last year that suggested her name, and I think you will agree that she has the speed of one.' Someone clapped, but the majority of his audience seemed to be concentrating longingly on some fixed point on the all too distant shore.

'She may have been built partly in Port Glasgow and partly in Glasgow itself,' continued Henry Bell, oblivious to the nervousness in his passengers, 'but you could lay down ships anywhere along the banks of the Clyde. You know, I believe paddle-steamers may one day be a familiar sight on the river, sailing regularly to Rothesay, Belfast, perhaps even further afield. I can see doubt in some of your faces, but the proof of the pudding's in the paddling. Now, we have a four-horse cylinder in operation, and while a tour of the engines of a paddle-boat on the Clyde may be a novelty, I know some of you will want to see them, so if you step this way with care please!'

Not knowing quite what to expect, the would-be sailors tottered off to see the engines.

HUNGER ROAD

It was the year 1847, the year of Charlotte Brontë's *Jane Eyre* and Thackeray's *Vanity Fair*. Marx had dotted the last 'i' and crossed the last 't' of the *Communist Manifesto*, and in Ireland, in Donnegal and Dungannon, in the west and in the green hills, the wailing of women, like the chill cry of a banshee on the moors, heralded the arrival of the potato famine.

The green island, so close to Britain and yet so different, had endured centuries of strife and war, but the blight that struck the potato crop was to starve and drive out nearly a quarter of the population. Some fled to America and Canada, while others crossed the water to Britain. Many arrived with nothing but the coats on their backs, and the passage to Glasgow was a sixpence they could ill afford. There was work, of a kind, for those willing to subject themselves to a 70-hour week, but there seemed no other way out for the people who had to leave their homes and tread the long miles of hunger road.

As soon as the sloop *General Wolfe* had cleared the harbour bar at Carrickfergus every plank and timber of her had started to creak with the merciless pounding of the storm that was raging in the Irish Sea. Driving rain and spray, inextricably mixed, deluged the decks as men clung to shrouds and tricing lines and stared wide-eyed through the torrents at the waves that seemed to be reaching up to suck them overboard into the deadly chill and quiet of the waters only a few feet below the screaming gale on the surface.

Below the bulkheads, in the hollow darkness of the groaning hull, the passengers sat close together for warmth and comfort, cowering with each new crash of the waves.

'There's water coming in, Sean,' said Bridey, wrapping

her shawl more tightly about the head of the screaming baby in her arms. 'See! There!' She nodded her head towards the water dripping steadily down from the bulkhead.

'What can I do about it?' Sean replied, straightening his back. 'If we are for going down, then that's all there is to it.'

'Don't say that,' she said unhappily.

'All right, I won't say it, but it's true anyway,' he replied.

She rocked back and forward, singing softly to the child. 'How could you abandon your own flesh and blood like that, God only knows,' she said reproachfully. 'Leaving your mother, Sean!'

'She was your mother,' he said. 'She was my mother-in-law.' He stood up, clutching an overhead beam to steady himself. 'I could see it all the way from Dungannon to Belfast. She wasn't up to the journey. She couldn't be persuaded, and I'd no mind to force her, poor old sowel.'

'I know you did your best,' said Bridey, relenting.

'And it was never good enough,' Sean answered bitterly. 'The town was like Hell itself on a Saturday, all those families from Ballygawley, Seskinore, Aughnacloy, Fintona and God knows where else, all together to celebrate the great starvation with a feast of leaving.'

'Talking like that willna give us a better life,' his wife said.

'No,' said Sean, watching the lamp swing backwards and forwards like a burning pendulum. 'No, it'll no' do that, but at least it's something to feed on.'

The baby started wailing again.

'Can you not stop the child?' Sean demanded.

'Can you?' answered Bridey crossly, cuddling the infant. 'What am I supposed to quieten her with? Answer me that! We're packed in this boat like cabbages in the landlord's store, and not a mouse's morsel between the lot of us.'

Sean sat down with a sigh and put his arm around his wife's shoulder. 'Bridey, Bridey,' he said sadly.

The baby quietened and looked up at him. Tiny fingers poked at his unshaven face and suddenly grasped hold of his nose. 'Ooya!' There were tears in Sean's eyes. 'You have a strong enough grip my wee darlin'. But Da needs his nose.' Gently he unclasped the baby's fingers and tucked them back inside the shawl. 'Look,' he said, turning to his wife, 'things will be better in Glasgow. I just know it. At least there'll be some kind of work.'

'Ye hope,' his wife replied dubiously. 'We all hope.'

Sean looked at his wife. She was twenty-three but could have been ten years older. 'There has to be work,' he said. 'There's that place Fergus telt us about.'

'What place?' replied Bridey wearily.

'That mill or somethin' at a place called Anderston.'

'If and when we ever get to land,' said Bridey, 'I'll be so glad to see solid earth that I'll hardly care what it's called.'

'Let's hope we get the peace and quiet to call it home,' her husband replied, as another great wave struck the ship.

Sean had been told to 'see a man' at Williamson's Cotton Mill on the corner of Stobcross Street and Cheapside Street, and he set off early from the attic room he had rented for his family near the Old Vennel. There was precisely nothing in his pocket. His last fourpence plus his jacket had gone towards the first week's rent of what was little better than a damp box on stilts, but they had to have somewhere, and he had to have a job. The first thing he had to do was find his way to Anderston, and, afraid of the police, he had got lost in a dark network of streets near the Saltmarket and eventually found himself by the river. The cold cabbage soup he had had the night before would not have been enough to nourish a beetle, never mind a full-grown man. Footsore and faint, he sat on the kerb near West Clyde Street and watched the carters carrying goods away from the ships that lined the river bank.

'Enjoying the view?' asked a voice beside him.

He turned and saw the owner of the voice was a small, bent figure in the remains of what had once been a splendid long brown overcoat. His head was bare but his whiskers and sideburns spread out on either side of his face like singed wings, making the strangely cherubic face look like a child peeping out from the middle of an overgrown gorse bush.

'I said, are ye enjoying the view?' the figure asked again.

'I would be,' answered Sean, 'except for the fact that I wish I'd never seen Glasgow.'

The man in the brown coat flopped down beside him like a sack of potatoes falling off the back of a lorry. 'I can tell by your accent,' he said, 'that you're from the Emerald Isle.'

'Are you trying to be funny, my friend?' Sean answered aggressively. ''Cause if you are, I think you should get about yer business, for I'm not too weak to give you an argument you won't like.'

'Now, now, now,' his companion said soothingly. 'No need to be like that. You're a stranger here, and I'm not. I'll help ye. That's what it's all about.'

'Is it?' Sean replied suspiciously.

'Of course it is, son,' said the man. 'Name's Bogle, Tam Bogle.' He held out a grimy hand.

After a moment's hesitation, Sean shook his hand.

'Where d'ye want to go?' asked Tam.

'Home,' answered Sean morosely, 'but for now I'll make do with the village of Anderston.'

Tam Bogle patted the side of his nose with his finger and winked alarmingly. 'Anderston?' he said. 'Did old Tam hear you say "Anderston"?'

'Right the first time,' replied Sean.

'Well,' said the man, 'go straight along here to the Broomielaw, turn up to your right along Robertson Street or Oswald Street, turn left, straight on and there ye are, canna miss it. Have ye got that?'

Sean stood up slowly and wearily. 'I think so,' he answered, 'but why are you helping me?'

'Well, suppose I met you one night in the place, wherever it is, that you come from, what would you do if I was lost?'

'Listen,' said Sean, 'the only way to get to where I come from is to be lost, but thanks, I'll not forget you.'

'That's what it's all about.' Tam Bogle grinned as Sean walked off towards the Broomielaw.

Sean had never seen a building like the mill before. It was bigger than a granary and taller than a church, and the noise of the machinery inside deafened him as he came along the street towards it, his mind a whirlpool of memories and doubts.

The man he had come to see was the clerk in the front office of the mill, and he had been told to ask for 'Billy Campbell' and give his name.

'I'm William Campbell,' said the man in answer to his query as he approached the desk. 'What did you say your name was?'

'Sean, Sean O'Donnel,' he replied.

William Campbell put his pen down and closed the ledger in front of him as if to prevent Sean from seeing what was in it. 'And what kind of a name is "Sean"?' he asked.

'That's my name, sir,' Sean answered. 'It goes with O'Donnel.'

The clerk frowned. 'If you are looking for work here,' he said slowly, 'you had best mind your manners, my friend. This here is a mill, a factory, understand? It's not a farm. What can you do?'

'Oh, I can turn my hand to most things, sir,' Sean said hopefully. 'I'll take on anything you have to offer.'

Campbell opened his book and consulted a list. He frowned, turning over a few pages slowly. 'Have you a family, O'Donnel?' he asked suddenly.

'Oh yes sir,' Sean smiled. 'Bridey, that's the wife, a wee one, and another on the way.'

Campbell appeared to make a mark in the book. 'Well this is no green hill in Ulster,' he said. 'This is the land of hard work. Can you give a 70-hour week, man?'

'Aye, sir,' said Sean eagerly. 'I'm willing to try anything.'

Campbell made another mark in his book. Sean thought that it must be a new kind of pen, because it never seemed to need dipping in the ink.

'I might be able to fit you in,' Campbell went on, 'but I'll have to speak to the old man, the master, first, and we have taken on a lot of you Irish already.'

'What kind of work would I be doing?' Sean asked.

'Why, labouring of course, what did you expect?' said the clerk.

'I'm good and strong,' Sean replied desperately.

Campbell made a wry face. 'You look more than half-starved to me. But maybe Glasgow will keep you from being hale-starved. Now, if I give you a start, or rather if the master gives you a start, no doing a moonlight.'

Sean looked puzzled.

'You are the green one,' Campbell continued. 'Moonlightin' is running out on your lodgings and not paying, but maybe I shouldna put such ideas into your head. Oh aye, there is one other matter. If you come to work here there is a small levy, a kind of tax.'

'Tax?' asked Sean.

Campbell looked at him slyly. 'Well you see, a job's a privilege, as I'm sure you understand with a wife and bairns.'

'Only one as yet,' the Irishman interrupted.

'That's as may be, but if you wish to start here, there is this levy to cover my, er . . . "expenses", do you understand me?'

Sean sagged visibly. 'Oh yes, sir. Very well,' he sighed.

'Well what d'you say,' said Campbell. 'A shilling a fortnight expenses to me and ye have a job. Take it or leave it.'

'It's a long way back to Ireland,' Sean replied. 'I'll take it.'

'Good,' grinned the clerk, dipping his pen in the inkwell. Make your mark and that's settled. You start the morn's morn, and mind, every fortnight regular.'

'Oh I'll remember sir,' said Sean, looking at the man's white collar and neat waistcoat. 'Don't you worry about that.'

FROM BALMANO STREET TO UJIJI

In the year 1835, two young students found themselves sharing rooms near the corner of Balmano Street and George Street, not far from the Andersonian. Each was destined in his own way to travel far on the road of knowledge and discovery, but one of them, a serious lad already sporting the beginnings of an enormous moustache, would travel further than most.

If there is any country in the world that might be described as a nation of voyagers and travellers, it's Scotland. As explorers, emigrants searching for a better life, missionaries and educators, Scots have ranged the world. Between the years 1835 and 1871, one of the two young men from No. 6 Balmano Street was to journey to the banks of the Zambezi River to Lake Ngami and the Victoria Falls; to search for the headwaters of the Nile; to be found at last at Ujiji; and to die in the region of Ilala in what is now Zambia. The boy who became the greatest explorer of the age belonged to Blantyre and Glasgow, but above all to the endless miles and mountains, the rivers and dark jungles of Africa, the mighty continent that still remembers his name.

As James Young pushed open the door of the small room with his knee, a cascade of books and pamphlets showered onto the floor. Kneeling to pick them up, he caught sight of his friend David grinning at him from beside the fireplace.

'When you said you were going to the library, I didn't think you meant you were going to bring it back with you,' said David, walking over and helping him gather up the scattered volumes.

'Thanks, Davy,' James said as they dumped the books in a heap on the large table in the middle of the room. 'Not a way to treat reading matter,' he went on, 'but if I don't get enough heat I think my fingers will fall off.'

'Oh well, there's not much chance of that, James my friend,' Davy replied, sitting down again on the stool by the fireplace and setting about snapping the remainder of the sticks lying by the hearth. 'The fire's not doing very well. I've been breaking sticks and hunting about for kindling since you went out. I can't seem to get warm.'

James looked down at the earnest figure crouched beside the dwindling flames. 'I'm cold because the wind tonight is like a knife,' he said, putting his hand on his friend's shoulder. 'With you, it's because you are overtired. You drive yourself too hard, man. Working in that noisy barn of a cotton-mill all day, studying and working with me at the Andersonian at night, and ye don't exactly let up when we get back here to Balmano Street. What time was it last night?'

David looked up at him sheepishly. 'I think about two, or maybe three,' he said.

'Well there you are,' James replied seriously. 'You should know better. You'll mak' yourself ill!'

'How else can a man learn except by work?' David Livingstone replied. 'These are difficult days, James. We have to do something to make things better, but first the thing is to learn!' His eyes burned with a dark intensity the equal of any fire. 'There's so much darkness in the world,' he added, poking the embers so that a brief rosy glow flickered across the walls of the bare room.

'And there'll be so much darkness in here if we don't get some oil for that lamp,' James Young replied. 'Now there's a question worth looking at, Davy. Oil. Mineral oil could be very important for Scotland one day. I was thinking today that oil fraction, paraffin and the like . . .'

'You are aye the chemist – James "Paraffin" Young,' laughed David Livingstone, interrupting him. 'You want to spread the message of your wonderful oils over the world, just as much as I feel a need to take my mission to Africa.'

'I wouldn't have put it like that,' James grinned at him.

'Well put these on the fire,' said David, thrusting his bundle of sticks into James' hands. 'Then maybe we can have some light and heat while we talk.'

James Young knelt down and pushed the sticks carefully into the mass of dull red embers. They both stared thoughtfully at the glow as tiny flames began to pierce and dance along the sticks, catching on drops of resin, retreating before the last of the wind that roared across the top of the chimney high above. The fire caught and the two young men sat on the floor, staring into the flames, secure in the comforting sight of those black and ruby castles of the imagination that have been with humankind since the beginning.

'You'll have plenty of heat if you go to Africa,' James Young said sleepily. 'From all accounts that I hear, the natives are as wild as their land.'

David Livingstone turned towards his friend. The homely glow softened his stern features like an island of evening in the winter. 'The "natives" you talk about are men, James,' he replied quietly. 'Men like ourselves. They just need some fuel to give out the light that's in them, that's all.'

James Young caught a new intensity, a note of decision in his companion's voice. 'Davy,' he said after a while. 'I really believe you are the man to give them their "light". That is, if ye actually get there.'

'Oh I will,' David replied. 'Africa is no dream for me, James. It's real, but it is dreaming. Maybe I can help to wake it up.' As he was speaking the handful of sticks that James Young had thrust into the fire began to give up, and the glowing embers drowned in a miniature flood of ashes.

'Ach!' exclaimed James angrily. 'That's it going out for good this time.'

David Livingstone stood up.

'What are ye doing?' said his friend, alarmed as David picked up the stool and brought it down on the floor with a crash.

'Firewood,' David answered simply.

'But that's your favourite seat, just about our only seat!'

James protested.

'If ye canna put away a favourite thing when you need to, then you are in chains,' David Livingstone replied, thrusting the broken wood into the fireplace. 'Come on,' he said, handing James a book. 'Let's study while we have the light and the heat.'

The young men sat, quietly turning the pages, while the wood hissed and cracked like a campfire in some undiscovered wilderness.

The waters of Lake Tanganyika shimmered in the midday heat, and a hot, dry breeze rattled the tall yellow grasses on the plain stretching north to the matted jungles of the Congo and southeast to the blue mountains of Tabora and Nyasaland. It was several days since the great herds of migrating wildebeest had passed north of the village, and now not even the vast clouds of dust remained to obscure the blazing blue of the tropical sky. The plain was dotted with the carcasses of the weak or sick, lying where they had fallen or where the swift cheetah had dashed to fell some straggler from the herd. A small circle of black specks were wheeling and dipping beside the cracked earth that had once been a water-hole far out across the savannah. The soundless motes rose suddenly and dived again to their feasting: vultures, watchful companions of any journey across the trackless miles of the enormous continent of Africa.

David Livingstone turned the page of his diary and sharpened his pencil. He hated to use it, but his precious pens had been lost somewhere between Kongolo and Nyangwe before he had even crossed Lake Tanganyika, and, as always, there were things that had to be written as well as said.

Suddenly a tribesman burst out of the undergrowth and ran across the clearing towards him. He recognized the man as Molonganeh, a runner and a warrior of the first rank.

'B'wana!' the man said, gasping for breath. 'B'wana Livingstone. Another . . . another white man coming!'

At first Livingstone didn't catch the flood of excited

85

words. 'What is it, Molonganeh?' he asked wearily. 'Can I not write my journal in peace?' Then, like a crack of summer lightning, he realized what the warrior had said. 'What did you say?' he exclaimed, gripping the side of his canvas chair. 'Another white man! Where? Who . . .?'

The tall African stamped his feet with impatience. He wore a loincloth of brilliantly coloured weave and anklets of antelope skin, and his face was like a dark pharaoh. He pointed excitedly down the hill past the threshing-floor towards the lake. 'I see him just now!' he said loudly, his deep voice booming across the clearing. 'He come up from the valley of the lion. Many bearers, many boxes, many guns, and one white man, white like you, B'wana Livingstone.'

Livingstone stood up slowly and peered through the shimmering haze towards the distant water. A long line of tribesmen was snaking its way slowly up the hill. Ahead of them and already striding towards him, hand outstretched, the stocky figure of a man, neat in his tropical whites, bore down on the astounded explorer.

'Good day, sir,' said the visitor expansively. 'Doctor Livingstone, I presume?'

David Livingstone took the man's hand and shook it like someone waking from a dream. 'Er, yes,' he said, taken aback. 'I am David Livingstone. Whom do I have the pleasure of . . .?'

The unexpected visitor grinned broadly. 'Stanley, sir,' he said. 'Henry Morton Stanley of the *New York Herald*.'

'Good Lord!' David Livingstone gasped, sitting down suddenly. 'You're not selling newspapers, are you?'

Stanley looked at him with concern. 'You look a trifle unwell,' he said.

The clearing was filling up with Stanley's bearers thumping their boxes and bags thankfully on the ground. They were joined by a milling crowd of curious villagers: young men, girls and matrons straight from the pottery or from flailing the grain, little knots of children laughing and dancing in circles about the stranger.

'I must apologise, sir,' Livingstone muttered. 'I had not

expected company.'

'Especially that of an American newspaper reporter, eh sir?' Stanley replied jovially.

'Well, not exactly,' agreed the Doctor.

'You, sir,' continued Stanley, unabashed, 'have led me across an entire continent from Cabinda to Bangala, along the entire length of the Congo River to Kindu, and finally here to Ujiji. The tribes everywhere know *who* David Livingstone is, but not *where*.'

'The search for the headwaters of the Nile has led me along some strange roads,' Livingstone replied. 'But tell me, Mr., er . . . Mr. . . .?'

'Stanley,' the reporter said obligingly.

'Aye, well, Mr. Stanley, sir. That's a marvellous journey you have made, but what exactly can I do for you?'

It was the turn of Henry Morton Stanley to be put out. 'Do, sir?' he asked in surprise. 'Why, I have come to rescue you.'

'Rescue me?' said David Livingstone quietly. 'From what, may I ask?'

Stanley recovered his poise like the professional he was. 'The entire civilized world,' he announced, 'not to mention the readership of my newspaper, has given you up for dead, sir.'

Livingstone smiled. 'You are implying that the world sets some value on my life.'

'You must be the only man in Africa, or anywhere else for that matter, who is unaware that David Livingstone is loved and venerated by millions who have learned the word of God at your hand, Doctor. You are a legend, sir.'

David Livingstone shook his head. 'No, no, Mr. Stanley,' he said. 'You are mistaken. Me? A legend? I would like to think that I have accomplished some of the things I came here to do, but a legend? Never! I'm just David Livingstone. If there is a legend you have just walked across it, Mr. Stanley: Africa. I am just a man on a journey, like yourself.'

ONCE MORE WITHOUT FEELING

The 1860s were half over. As tenements, houses, yards and workshops covered what had been green hills only a few years previously, Glasgow turned into a 'dear grey place', and the clouds at night were lit with the glow of burning slag as the forges and bellows worked ceaselessly to supply the needs of an enormous and growing empire.

With the end of the Civil War in America slavery had been abolished, but there was another kind of bondage all over the world, the tyranny of infection. People died from even the simplest cut or wound, and to undergo surgery meant almost certain death.

Joseph, later Lord, Lister held the Chair of Surgery at Glasgow University. He also held what were regarded as rather unorthodox views. He had been experimenting for some time with ways of controlling the 'microbes of infection' that Louis Pasteur had written about. He realized that these were the source of the infection in wounds that became gangrenous after an operation, and tried desperately to find some way to prevent the invisible scourge of germs from killing more than half his patients in Glasgow's Royal Infirmary. He used a number of approaches, including filtration, heat, and chemicals. Eventually he discovered that a mixture of crystallized carbolic acid and shellac, or 'lac plaster', and later, calico painted with a solution of benzine, would improve chances of recovery after an operation enormously. He later developed the carbolic spray, and was well on the road to a true 'antiseptic' that would free surgery from the realms of chance. He only needed the opportunity to prove its effectiveness. One hot day in August 1865 that opportunity arrived.

The stacatto rattle of iron-rimmed cart wheels over the bumpy cobbles mingled with the cries of street-hawkers and the chatter of passers-by. Great heavy drays lumbered down the brae of the High Street towards the bonds at the foot of the Cross, and the air was heavy with the smell of smoke and the bitter tang of yeast. Giant Clydesdales strained in the traces, four for going down the hill and sometimes as many as eight to come up it.

James Greenlees had been out playing since early in the morning. Together with several other boys, he had waded the Molendinar. There was no problem about his shoes. He didn't have any. They had looked for last year's chestnuts in the green hollow by Tennant's, dodged in and out of the traffic, and finally sat down on the pavement in front of the Cathedral, exhausted.

James lived across the road in the Drygate, and from where he sat he could just make out this evening's bowl of broth cooling on the windowsill. His stomach rumbled and he realized he was more than a little hungry.

'Aye, James,' said his best friend Womfer, tapping him on the shoulder. 'Here's yer auld dear comin'.'

James' mother had just emerged from the close across the road and was standing, hands on hips, peering across the busy street in his direction.

'James Greenlees!' she bawled, waving her hands in the air. 'You're to come in for a piece and jam!'

Womfer chuckled sardonically. 'That's you caught.'

'Och, it's too early,' James complained.

'James! Will you get over here this minute!' his mother called out again.

'I'll need to go, lads,' James said.

Mrs. Greenlees was becoming apoplectic. 'Ya wee monkey!' she cried. 'Get ower here this minute!'

'Aw, Ma!' James shouted back, 'I'm playin' with ma freens!'

His mother took a step towards the traffic, thought better of it, and stayed where she was. 'You're for a right leatherin' when your Da gets hame,' she called.

'See you later boys,' James said sadly, stepping out into

the traffic.

A gigantic wagon rolled down the hill, the driver's mate straining at the brakes as the enormous load trundled along, picking up speed. Sparks flew from the iron-shod wheels, and the horses sweated and snorted in the traces.

'Here I'm comin' Ma!' James shouted again as he ran across the road.

He never heard his mother's terrified screams or the driver's curses, as his world turned suddenly, sickeningly, upside-down. The smell of horses and beer, hot wood and metal seemed to overwhelm him. Somehow, far away, someone was lighting a fire below his left knee as he began falling into a black pit. 'Funny,' he thought to himself before all thought vanished. 'I never knew there was a great big hole in the middle of the street.'

Distant sounds of traffic filtered past the tall hospital windows as sleepers struggled from dream to dream. Nurses walked softly down the long aisle, closing the curtains in front of the box-beds as Joseph Lister neared the end of his round of the Surgical Ward.

'This wee boy's very bad,' the nurse said softly, stopping by the last bed but one.

As if to confirm what she had been saying, the small figure stirred restlessly and cried out. 'Ma! I want my Ma!'

Joseph Lister bent over the wee boy. 'Laudanum?' he asked without looking up.

'The amount you prescribed, Professor Lister,' the nurse said, pulling the sheet back from the cage and revealing the bent and swollen limb. Fragments of cloth, dark with dried blood, still adhered to the boy's leg which lay twisted to one side like a child's drawing of a clown on broken stilts.

'We will have to cut all this away,' Lister whispered. He took the scissors the nurse held out and began cutting, carefully snipping the fragments of torn cloth trouser away from the terrible injury. 'Bad!' he said as more of the wound came into view. 'A compound fracture of the worst kind. It will have to be re-set. I'll need your assistance with this,

Jean.'

'Which way is it to go?' the nurse asked doubtfully.

'To the right,' he replied with a frown. 'Steady now. We have to break it again.'

They took hold of the little boy's foot firmly.

'That's it. Ready to turn the foot right, Jean. Now!'

There was a sudden wrenching, cracking sound, like damp twigs tearing and splitting under some unbearable weight. The boy moaned in his laudanum-induced dreams as Jean leaned forward to swab the injury clean.

'Wash it very well,' Professor Lister said. 'I'm going to use the new dressing.'

'You mean the carbolic?' the nurse asked, raising her eyebrows.

'I mean the carbolic,' he said with an air of finality. 'It's that or watch the wound fester and turn gangrenous.'

'If you can stop the infection that follows a fracture like this, Professor, you have saved the wee boy's life,' the nurse replied, her cloth staining the water red as she squeezed it into the bowl.

'We will know in a day or two,' Lister said, standing up stiffly. 'It's the first time that I've used it in a case like this, so if he's anything for the worse, let me know at once.'

The nurse nodded as he walked away, a tall figure dressed in black, the golden hands of the surgeon thrust deep into his baggy pockets.

James Greenlees blinked at the light as the curtains around the bed were drawn back. He could see barred windows high up, and beyond, the light blue of the August sky.

'And how is he today?' a man's deep voice asked somewhere to his left.

'There's tissue forming over the wound, Professor Lister,' a woman answered. 'As yet, there's no sign of any infection.'

Out of the corner of his eye James glimpsed two shapes, one small and fair, the other tall, dark and forbidding. The grim, shadowy figure leaned over him. 'Well then, let's have a look,' the man said. 'What's you're name, eh?'

There was a sudden stabbing in James' knee. 'James . . . ooya! . . . Greenlees, mister,' he replied through gritted teeth.

'That hurts, does it?' the surgeon asked in a kindly voice. 'Well, Mr. Greenlees, the Royal Infirmary will soon have you back on your feet.'

James looked up at him, wide-eyed. 'Am I gaun tae die mister?' he asked.

'No, no, of course not!' Lister exclaimed. 'Now, do you see that clock at the end of the ward?'

'Aye, mister,' James replied brightly.

'Well then,' said Professor Lister. 'You can tell the time, big boy like you?'

'Oh aye,' James grinned. 'It's just coming up to . . .'

Lister interrupted him. 'Well you just keep looking at it,' he said. 'I just want a wee look at that leg of yours.'

James cried out in pain. 'Now don't be silly,' the surgeon scolded him, peering at the boy's knee. 'What time is it?'

'It, it's a quarter to . . . Ooya!' James yelped.

Lister smiled at him. 'Well, my young lad. I've got some good news for you. You have survived a very serious injury and there is no infection.'

'What does that mean?' James asked.

Lister stood up and looked at the other patients ranged down each side of the long ward. 'It means,' he replied slowly, 'that others can do the same. Thank you, lad.'

'Whit fur?' asked James, puzzled.

'For being a good boy. Now lie down and get some rest,' the Professor said genially, patting him on the head.

'I didn't do nuthin',' James said again, still mystified.

'You have lived through a crisis in your blood,' smiled Lister, straightening his coat.

'Here!' said James Greenlees, sitting up suddenly. 'I'll get a right leatherin' when I get hame!'

THE GOLD AND SULPHUR WIZARD

As years became decades, Victorian pride and confidence moved swiftly towards its noon, and the enterprise and energy of the age became embodied in the entrepreneurs and adventurers of industry. As much as steam and electricity, a new power source for the manufacturing explosion was the energy of men like Charles Tennant. While he was still a young man, he had become a partner in his grandfather's firm, and by 1866, he was Director of the Tharsis Sulphur and Copper Company. Tennant's combination of imagination, organizational ability and ruthlessness found its ultimate expression in the forest of chimneys at the St. Rollox works, where he consolidated an empire that was eventually to form, together with other companies, the basis of the multinational I.C.I. Here was a man who could order the exploration of some new idea, and designers, engineers, craftsmen and workers of all kinds would develop, test and build the form and substance of an engine, a bridge or a train from the first scribblings on paper to the gleaming, complex, noisy reality. The Victorian Age, a strange mixture of top hats and mechanical genius, owes its character and its success to the millions who laboured ceaselessly to create the products of the new industry, but above all to the driving force of men like the 'Gold and Sulphur Wizard'.

It was siesta time in Alosno and every shutter was shut against the glare of the afternoon sun. The alleys were full of the smell of hot stone and almendras blossom, cats dozed in forgotten gardens and passion fruit and avocado grew untended by the dried-up river bed that skirted the ruined convent of Our Lady of Sorrows.

The coach rattled down the blistering road, its single

occupant sweating in the dark interior, occasionally peering out of the dusty window at the yellow and black landscape and the approaching orange-tiled roofs of the sleeping town. The driver raced through the quiet streets, scarcely slowing as he rounded the Plaza Major, and rumbled past the shuttered Officina Postales and the tiny Ristorante Juan Cobilla. A sleepy eye peered out from behind a shutter as the coach rattled through the pueblo and up the hill towards the Tharsis Sulphur and Copper Mine at the top of the barranco.

Andrew held his safety lamp out in front of him at arm's length as he struggled down the tunnel towards the second level. 'Mr. Dougalston! Mr. Dougalston!' he called out excitedly, and the echoes ran along the hollow chambers, infinite mirrors of sound that finally vanished into the subterranean deeps far under the mountain.

Without warning he found himself at a junction in the passage. To the left was only more darkness, but on the right and down he saw other lights, bobbing as men worked and sweated in the arid gloom. He heard the strident voice of the mine manager, cursing in a combination of Scots, French, and rudimentary Spanish. The inelegant lingua franca bounced off the sulphurous walls like nails in a tin.

'Mas rapido, enfant!' shouted the manager. 'Youse hombres have never heard of work, have ye's? Trabacho, n'that! Trabacho! Come on well!'

'Here's the visitor comin',' Andrew called breathlessly as he ran up to him. 'I saw him comin' up to the entrance and gettin' out of his coach.'

Mr. Dougalston rounded on him impatiently. 'That's the last thing I need just now!' His voice rang hollowly. 'A tourist from Glasgow. Well, if he takes exception to the props, I'll just have to tell him straight out. The Rio Tinto's bought up the surplus.'

'He's not exactly a tourist,' Andrew replied. 'He's the owner.'

Dougalston glared at him in the half-light. 'No, he's no'!' he said with emphasis. 'He's the Director, and how the devil I'm supposed to ca' the sulphur out with this equipment and these men, I've no idea.'

His final words were drowned out by a frenetic thumping. Small cascades of pebbles, shaken loose by the vibration, poured down onto their feet and piled up beside the rough props supporting the weight of the mountain overhead. Dougalston swore under his breath. 'Here! Parada!' he shouted at the men further down the tunnel. 'Stop for God's sake! Ye'll have the hale thing down on us!' For answer, a cloud of dust billowed towards them out of the depths, setting both men coughing. 'Por favor an' all that!' Dougalston roared, charging off into the echoing dust-cloud.

After a few minutes he returned, slapping his shoulders free of the sulphurous grit. 'That's that team up from Alosno,' he said, shaking his head.

Andrew emerged from behind the shoring where he had been hiding and nodded agreement, his eyes still wide with fear. 'A pack of nae-users,' Dougalston went on like a man who daily fights a mountain, and wins. 'They'll have the Tharsis in about our ears, and that's a fact.'

'Aye, Mr. Dougalston,' Andrew agreed, shuddering. 'I thought we were for it that time.'

Dougalston laughed and thumped the boy hard between the shoulder blades, raising a cloud of dust that made them both sneeze. 'Ach, yer all right son,' he grinned.

Andrew looked at him. 'It's that Rio Tinto luring the men away with more money,' he said sagely.

The mine manager shook his head in disgust. 'Nae shoring or props,' he complained, 'Nae workers that I can rely on. Am I supposed to dig the pyrites out with my bare hands? Am I?' He poked Andrew in the ribs with a broad, earthy finger.

'I don't know,' Andrew replied with a nervous laugh, fear of Mr. Dougalston struggling with loyalty to the Company. 'I just do what I'm told sir. Maybe Mr. Tennant will ...'

'Him?' interrupted the manager in a loud voice. 'What does he know about mining?'

'Well, gentlemen? Did I hear my name being taken in vain?' Charles Tennant walked towards them, his guide scurrying ahead. 'Sound carries a long way in here.'

'Oh, oh, Mr. Tennant,' said Andrew, flustered. 'I was just after saying you were on your way here and . . .'

With a painful thud the tall man banged his head on an outcropping of rock.

'Oh watch your head, sir,' Andrew exclaimed solicitously.

'A top hat is obviously not the headgear for a Spanish mine,' Charles Tennant moaned, taking his rather dented hat off and rubbing the side of his head ruefully.

'Do you want to sit down, sir?' Dougalston asked warily.

'Dougalston, isn't it?' Tennant peered at him in the wavering light. 'No thank you, man. I'll be all right in a moment, but the air is bitter down here.'

'That's the sulphur fumes, Mr. Tennant. You get used to them after a while,' the manager replied.

Squeezing the dent out of his hat and putting it on, Charles Tennant looked at the sloping walls on either side curiously. 'Well sulphur and pyrites are what I'm here about Mr. Dougalston,' he said firmly. 'I was told at the entrance that this was the main shaft. There's not much mining in progress here. Is there some problem that I should know about?'

Dougalston gestured behind them with his thumb. 'It's them back there,' he said, 'the blasted, beggin' your pardon sir, Rio Tinto. Can I speak plain, sir?'

'I insist that you do,' Tennant frowned at him.

'Well,' Dougalston began. 'It's a long story, but I'll be brief . . .'

'I insist on that as well.' Tennant smiled without humour.

'Well,' Dougalston began again, taken aback. 'They, that's the Tinto, are the main rivals for us here at the Tharsis.'

'That much I know,' said the visitor impatiently. 'It's one of the main reasons I've come all the way from Glasgow to Spain. To see exactly what is going on down here.'

'The competition is verra fierce,' the manager replied, shaking his head.

'I think,' Charles Tennant said with slow confidence, 'that you can leave the competition to me. What I do want to know about is the, er, the "other" matter you wrote to Head Office about.'

'What other matter, sir?' Dougalston asked. 'Ah, yes, that other matter.' Realization dawned on him. He turned to Andrew, who had been standing at a respectful distance while the two men talked. 'Andrew!' he said with a nod and a wink. 'Go and see if the new pit props have arrived.'

Andrew looked at him in amazement. 'But there are no new pit props, Mr. Dougalston,' he protested.

'Do as you are telt, Andrew,' Mr. Dougalston answered, a note of menace in his voice.

Andrew turned and walked slowly back up the tunnel. As he went they could hear him muttering to himself. 'I'll have a look, but there's nane I'm tellin' you.'

Dougalston's voice dropped to a whisper. 'That's him away now, Mr. Tennant. A good worker, but no' very bright. We're all right now. These Spanish lads canna understand good plain Scots.'

'Tell me, in English or Scots. Your report spoke of precious metals in the ores?' There was a hint of excitement in Tennant's voice.

'That's it sir,' Dougalston replied blandly. 'It's my opinion, having been in this business for many years like, that as well as the pyrites there's a good deal of silver and maybe even gold down here.'

'Then let's go back to the surface and you can tell me in detail,' said the industrialist, turning to go.

'Watch yer heid, sir!' the manager cried.

'If what you said is true,' said Tennant crossly, 'then perhaps the headache of this place will be worth it.' Hat in hand, he made his way warily through the heavy gloom. When he emerged, the bare pinnacles of rock that ringed the Tharsis ravine were tipped with the Spanish gold of a late summer evening.

The chimneys of St. Rollox belching out their black smoke were like a forest of pillars holding up a storm. It was 1880, and in the intervening years a giant factory had grown up, filled with the incessant clamour of casting, the bubbling of chemical vats, and the clang of steam-hammers.

The two men stood on the narrow catwalk like flies on a curtain rail and looked down at the throb and clatter of the vast workshops.

'Changed days, Charles,' said Sir Michael Connal, raising his voice over the surging noise. 'You, myself, Baird. We will end up being the workshop of the world!'

'I think we are that already,' Sir Charles Tennant said in his ear. 'But your family connections have been doing that for centuries.'

Sir Michael nodded. Down below an army struggled with raw chemicals and liquid metal. 'Indeed, Charles,' he agreed. 'We managed the city during the Jacobites' ten days, traded in tobacco when we were Cunninghams, and now, well, the Iron Ring can only get bigger.'

'It is to be hoped so,' Sir Charles Tennant shouted back. 'But the Kolar field has helped this firm as much as chemicals and iron.'

Sir Michael looked at his friend out of the corner of his eye. 'A gold mine in Spain and another in India would help anyone, Charles. But what exactly do you think we should do about this proposal for a railway bridge?'

'Over the Forth?' Sir Charles asked, stroking his beard. 'If we go in, and it is "if" at the moment, I can bring to the job some of my engineers who have been working on the railway in America.'

Sir Michael Connal looked at him with respect. 'Sulphur, chemicals, gold, steel,' he laughed. 'I think if you were asked to build a tunnel under the Channel, you'd make a start on Monday, Charles.'

'This is only the middle of the week,' said Sir Charles Tennant with a twinkle in his eye. 'Why wait till Monday?'

A TOKYO FOR TEAROOMS

It was 1899 and Glasgow was approaching the closing days of the century in a mood of careful optimism. Wealth and culture had built and decorated a great sandstone metropolis that had become the 'Second City of the Empire'. The pace of invention was accelerating like a runaway tobogganist on buttered ice, and H.G. Wells' *Time Machine* and *War of the Worlds* were hinting at the future. It was an age of opulence and aspidistras, but also an age of grinding poverty. The Boer War and the new century were to come in together, and the sheer solidity of Glasgow on the eve of the twentieth century was already cracking at the base like the great glazed ceramic fountain in Kelvin Park, as guns and colonists, men and machines battled for a place in the sun in Africa and the plains and peninsulas of Asia. In addition to war and science, and in a sense above them, that age-old science of the imagination, Art, was changing also. A new style and a new form had developed called 'Art Nouveau'.

Inspired by the art of Japan, designers and architects had begun to adopt the delicate romantic forms they associated with the East, marrying them with Pre-Raphaelite notions of an impossible medieval world and the real world of soaring and elongated Gothic. The Japanese woodcuts and ceramics that were becoming so fashionable were actually not the fruits of a world of delicacy alone. They came from a very different culture from that of Europe, and in Nippon the same society which revered blossom floating in swollen rivers also made the terrifying war-masks of the Shogun and followed the deadly way of the Ninja and the Samurai – the Code of Death. But the knights of the new art in the West were not the Knights of Bushido. They saw what they liked then copied and developed it, and a new style was born for the new century.

Charles Rennie Mackintosh, Glasgow artist and architect, was possessed of a unique and multi-faceted genius. The Art Nouveau movement had begun in the nineties, and Charles Rennie had made of it something uniquely his own. No one who has ever looked up at the facades of the Glasgow School of Art can doubt that this Glasgow man, whose style had a profound influence in France, Germany and Austria, was making what is essentially Scottish architecture. As well as 'Art Nouveau', Mackintosh buildings are 'Baronial Nouveau'. By 1899 the East Wing of the new Art School was complete, and Mackintosh and his friends had begun to be involved in projects like the re-decoration and design of Glasgow's dismal eating houses. It was only fitting that art from the land of the tea ceremony should inspire the new-style meeting places that Mackintosh designed for his friend Kate Cranston.

There were ferns of frost on the panes of the gas-lamps as Rennie Mackintosh made his way carefully up the steep slippery hill of Dalhousie Street towards the winged parapets of the towering East Wing of the Glasgow School of Art. His steps became slower as he neared the top of the hill and turned the corner into Renfrew Street with a thankful sigh. As he walked towards the entrance of the half-completed building, the railings and wrought-iron brackets stood out starkly against the fresh clean sandstone of the facade and frost and snow highlighted the decorative flowers and curlicues with touches of silver and white.

The enormous heavy doors swung open at a push and he walked across the hall. 'Excuse me, is Mr. Herbert McNair about?' he asked the janitor.

'He's along in the life studio. Drawing the female,' the man replied, resplendent in his bottle-green coat.

Mackintosh started to walk down the long corridor.

'Hold on sir!' called the janitor. 'You can't go in there! It's just for artists.'

Mackintosh stopped and turned round. 'I am an artist,

sir!' he said crossly.

'Oh that's what they all say, sir,' the janitor replied firmly. 'I'm just doing my job.'

'Have you worked here long?' Charles Rennie asked, peering at the man's face.

'I'm just temporary, like. Replacing James Bayliss while he's sick.'

Mackintosh smiled. 'Tell me, janitor, do you know who designed this building?'

'The School of Art?' replied the man uncertainly. 'Er, perhaps if you care to ask at the office yonder . . .'

Mackintosh took a watch from his pocket, looked at it, and put it back again. 'They would likely say it was somebody called Mackintosh,' he said softly. 'Charles Rennie Mackintosh.'

'I really couldn't say, sir. But if you would like to give me your name while you are waiting for Mr. McNair, I'll see he gets your message.'

'The name's Charles Rennie Mackintosh,' the architect said with mock-seriousness.

The temporary janitor became very flustered. 'Oh, oh, I'm awfully sorry, Mr. Mackinslash,' he stammered.

'"Tosh", sir, as in coats of the same name,' Mackintosh grinned.

'Sorry, Mr. Coats, I mean, I should say . . .' He was interrupted by the hollow ringing of the telephone bell attached to the wall. 'That's the telephone in my box,' he said with relief. 'I'll need to go, sir.'

'Fine,' replied the architect. 'I'll just make my own way to the life studio.'

'Very good,' answered the man in the green coat, beating a hasty retreat. 'Sorry about that, Mr. Mackintash.'

The corners of the enormous high-ceilinged studio were dark, but the pale winter light filtered in through the tall windows and fell on the centre of the floor in a pool of silver. A pink, dark-haired figure sat very still in a carved chair just where the light was brightest, and arranged in a semi-circle round about her, a dozen students worked in utter silence. Mackintosh looked across the room. His friend Herbert McNair was sitting near a large canvas screen watching a young student make broad, sweeping strokes with the charcoal on a sheet of hand-made paper.

Herbert looked up as Mackintosh approached. 'Hello, Charles,' he said softly. 'Won't be a minute. I'll just finish having a word with our friend here and tell the model to get dressed.' He turned to the young student beside him. 'You see,' he said quietly, 'it's not a body, it's paper, and it's your job as an artist to explain what you see to me and the rest of the world, not to mention Mr. Mackintosh here.' He smiled up at his friend. 'What do you think?' he asked.

Mackintosh looked at the boy's drawing. 'Quite a nice line,' he replied slowly, 'but you haven't caught the way her shoulders slope more to one side than the other. May I?' He took a piece of charcoal from a nearby desk.

There was a low groan from the centre of the room, followed by a heavy thud.

Herbert looked up in surprise. 'Oh Lord! The model's fainted.' Not quite sure what to do, the younger students put down their drawing-boards and stared. Herbert and Charles walked quickly over to the still figure.

'Is she all right?' Mackintosh asked, trying to get her to sit up.

'She fell on the mattress,' Herbert replied. 'Just a bit dizzy, I think.'

The model groaned again, blinked, and opened her eyes wide. 'Whit's happenin'?' she asked shakily.

'There now, dear,' Herbert said comfortingly, putting a brocade cloth from a nearby still-life around her shoulders. 'Away you go and get your clothes on. I don't think these girls eat very much, Charles,' he said as she shuffled behind the canvas screen.

Mackintosh nodded. 'These Greek positions are too much for the women,' he agreed. 'They need more rests.'

'It's this School of Art of yours, Charles,' Herbert said with a wink. 'It's too perfect. It makes people forget the passage of time.'

'Speaking of which, we should have been in Argyle

Street an hour ago,' Mackintosh replied.

'Kate!' said Herbert. 'I forgot we had to be at the tearoom. I asked the janitor to remind me.'

'That explains it then,' Charles said with a grin.

The sound of polite conversation and the ring of bone china filled Kate Cranston's Argyle Street Tearooms. Charles Rennie Mackintosh, his future wife Margaret Macdonald, her sister Frances, Herbert McNair and Kate Cranston sat by a fine filigree screen like a geometric forest, talking earnestly among themselves.

'But all your work is beautiful, Charles,' Kate Cranston said with a smile. 'Even the Earl Grey tastes better. There was a gentleman in here yesterday all the way from New York who thought it all quite, quite delightful.'

'The tea?' Mackintosh asked, pouring himself another cup.

'Now don't be silly,' Kate Cranston scolded him. 'He is being silly, isn't he, Margaret?' Margaret Macdonald gave her a knowing look.

'You know what I'm talking about, Charles,' Kate continued. 'I mean your beautiful decorations. And your panels, Margaret. Everything, colours, furniture, even teaspoons.'

'I still say that the Japanese style has the strongest influence on us all, Charles,' Herbert said, handing him the Viennese gateau.

Charles lifted a piece with the tongs, put it on his plate and broke the corner off speculatively with his fork. 'Not Japanese, Herbert,' he replied after a moment. It's a new art all on its own, an "Art Nouveau".'

'Well,' said Herbert, helping himself to the cake. 'Japanese or not, even you must admit that Glasgow is turning into a Tokyo for tearooms.'

TAKE ME TO THE FLICKERS

In the early 1900s Glasgow was, as it had always been, a place for shows of all kinds, for music hall, mystery and mummery. With the opening of the new century a new kind of entertainment had begun to arrive in the city. People called it the 'flickers', but no one could describe it very well, except to say that it was exciting, even frightening. The only way to sample its delights, or otherwise, was actually to go and see for yourself. The 'flicker shops' were the forerunners of the 'pichers', and the show that was to go on from the silents to the talkies (when Glasgow would have more cinemas than any other city in Europe) began, appropriately enough, in wee back shops round a corner or some room or other off a close.

The crossing leading from Parly Road towards Alexandra Parade and Castle Street up towards Springburn was one of the busiest in Glasgow. All kinds of people and vehicles milled about in a confusion that would have made a fire in an anthill look like a Sunday School outing for wooden soldiers. Soldiers were actually the cause of the stramash on that particular wet May morning in long-ago 1904. Military bands had become a more frequent sight in the city since the Boer War, symptoms of a European tension that seemed to erupt into crises and international incidents every second week.

'Ye missed a rare march-past, Wull,' said wee Dick as his friend sauntered past towards the shops at the bottom of the road.

'Oh aye,' replied the older boy sullenly. 'That's fine. I canna stop. I've been sent a message for my Uncle Wally.'

'Is that the man with dugs?' asked Dick brightly. 'Wally dugs, eh?'

Wull looked as though he was about to burst into tears. 'That's fine,' he said again mournfully.

'What's up wi' ye, drippy?' asked the irrepressible Dick. 'My cousin's jined the army. Is that no' good?'

'Good for him then,' replied the dismal Wull. 'You away an' play soldiers tae, Dick. I've got ma message tae go.'

'It must be some message,' sneered the little boy. 'Anyway, see your Uncle Wally? He's no' your right uncle at all. He's your ma's bidey-in. Bidey-in, bidey-in,' he yelled in a sing-song voice.

Wull was stung into action and took a swipe at him with his greasy striped cap. Dick ducked and ran up a nearby close, still laughing and jeering. A solitary 'bidey-in' came wafting back from the drying green, then he was gone.

'I'll see you efter, Dick Malloy,' Wull yelled at the empty street.

'What's up, Wull?' asked Champer Gilhooly. 'Yer lookin' a bit down in thon thing you put hoat pies in.'

'Oh, it's yourself, Champer,' Wull said. 'It's that wee Dick givin' us cheek.' He heaved a deep sigh. 'That lodger we've got in the now. He's aye sayin', "Away you go and play, son," or sending me out for beer.'

Champer nodded wisely. 'That's what it's all about.'

'What is?' asked Wull blankly.

'Och, life and things like that,' said the grubby sage. 'Here! The gang's away up to the Necropolis to play at Wild Bill Cody efter. Comin'?'

'I widna' mind,' Wull replied sadly, but . . . no, I canna. I've got threepence to get his beer, and Ma'll gie me laldy if I'm late, so she will, and so will himself and all.'

'Come on, well,' wheedled Champer. 'You'll like as not get a leatherin' just for luck when you get hame.'

A silent battle raged beneath the greasy cap as Wull fought with himself. 'Och I should'na,' he said at last. 'Och, maybe I will. I hate uncles.'

'Right ye are then,' Champer grinned, 'we're all meeting down the hill by the bone shop.'

'The hospital?' Wull asked.

'Naw, naw, naw!' Champer replied impatiently. 'The Cathedral. Can ye no' unnerstaun' English?'

'All right then,' said Wull, surrendering. He fell in with his friend and they walked briskly down Glebe Street towards Cathedral Street, pausing to look enviously at the display of apples outside the grocer's.

'They're from Canada, you know,' said Champer with a professorial air.

'Away ye go,' Wull replied. 'That's further away than Edinburgh. They'd all be rotten by the time they got here.'

'Not a bit of it,' Champer said, shaking his head. 'Big Sandy Broon says they can do anything they want these days, now that everythin's mair modern.'

'All right then,' Wull challenged him. 'How do they put a ship in a bottle?'

'Oh, weel now,' Champer replied with a frown. 'That's more yer actual science and all that.'

'Don't know, eh?' Wull grinned.

'I bet you don't know what goes on in that new place at the corner of Castle Street,' Champer countered smugly.

'Aye I dae,' Wull replied with defiance.

'Tell's then,' his friend grinned.

'Och!' Wull scratched his head. 'What is it then?'

'Well,' said Champer with a secretive wink. 'It's in the back of Moffat's the Chemist. He's callin' it "The Palace", but it's just the back shop, really.'

'What is?' asked Wull, his curiosity aroused.

'The flickers is, that's what,' Champer replied. 'It's some kind of show or something. It's supposed to be frightening. Listen! I've got tuppence-ha'penny from helpin' Crusty the Baker, and you've got your threepence. Dae ye fancy a look?'

'I'd better not spend *his* money,' Wull said doubtfully.

'If yer afraid, that's a different story, Wull,' Champer leered.

Wull squared his shoulders and drew himself up to his full three foot six inches. 'I'm no' afraid of nuthin',' he said, puffing out his chest. 'Not Zulus, not lions, not even Uncle Wally. Come on!'

The back of Moffat's chemist shop was full of people. A large wooden box had been placed by the far wall, and on it stood a strange machine like a small bicycle, but upside down. On the wall opposite to it had been pinned a large linen sheet, and a motley assortment of chairs and boxes had been arranged in neat rows. In the front row, perched on a couple of tea-chests, Wull and Champer sat staring at the cloth hanging on the wall in front of them.

Without warning the gas was turned down low and, as if operated by the same mechanism, conversation dropped to a minimum.

'Psst! Champer!' Wull whispered in the darkness. 'I just hope this is worth it, that's all. I canna see nuthin'.'

'Wait will ye?' replied the older boy.

'Well I canna see a thing in here,' Wull whispered again. 'This back shop is no' big enough to swing a hellypotamus in.'

'A whit?' Champer asked in surprise.

'One of thae great beasts that eat ye over in the colonies,' Wull replied with the air of one who knows. 'Ye know ye get man-eatin' vultures as well?'

'Aye, very good,' replied Champer. 'Shut up will ye?'

'I still say this place is no' big enough,' said Wull, offended.

'Big enough for whit?' Champer moved his tea-chest to one side a little.

'Och, for whatever it is that's goin' to happen, that's what. If anything is going to happen,' Wull added lugubriously.

'Shhh!' said someone sitting behind Champer, poking him in the back.

'It was him!' complained Champer, pointing to Wull.

'Naw I never,' said Wull, snorting at the bitter injustice of life.

'Here's auld Mr. Moffat comin',' whispered Champer, 'Now you'll see somethin'.' There was a rattle of tins and a rustle of celluloid from the back of the room. 'That's the flicker thing he's fixing the now,' said Champer. 'See! He's lightin' the paraffin lamp!'

'Ya cheat!' Wull exclaimed. 'You've been here afore!'

'Just the wance,' Champer muttered in an off-hand manner.

Mr. Moffat's creaking voice came from the area of the clanking and rustling. His nickname among the local urchins was 'Auld Spider' or simply 'Creepy', and as he stood at the back of the room, his thin face lit from beneath by the fugitive glow of the lamp-housing of his machine, he lived up to every last chill he had ever sent down any Townhead spine. 'Just a moment, ladies and gentlemen,' he said with a dry wheeze. 'I just have the reel to attach and the film to thread.'

There were more rattles and scratching sounds. Wull turned angrily to Champer now visible in the half-light from the machine. 'Reel? Thread?' he said. 'Is this a sewing lesson?'

The machine began to emit a steady whirr. 'Naw,' Champer replied. 'Look! Look in front of ye!'

Wull looked. Where there had only been a limp sheet hanging on the wall like a piece of forgotten washing there was an enormous window. He was looking at a broad, rolling plain with low dusty hills in the distance. Across the flat land stretched a gleaming railway line. On it, charging directly at him, smoke and sparks belching out of its tapering smoke-stack, was a huge, solid-looking railway engine. 'L . . . Look! Look at that!' he gasped.

'Aye, I see it,' replied Champer smugly. 'A railway train.'

'But it's comin' towards us,' screamed Wull, leaping up from his seat. 'We'll be run over, KILLED!'

'Dinna be daft,' said Champer, pulling him down onto the tea-chest again. 'It's not real. See! Yer heid's makin' a big black shadow on it. It's silent, see! Sit down and enjoy yerself. We're at the flickers.'

A TRAM DRIVER'S CHRISTMAS IN
FRANCE

The world was at war. After the deluge that decided the
first battle of Ypres was over in the second week of
November 1914, King George V arrived at Saint-Omer in
Northern France, H.Q. of the British Expeditionary Force.
What he saw shocked him, but the war continued and the
days and deaths rolled inexorably on towards the end of
that first, bitter year. Then it was Christmas on the
Western and Eastern fronts, the Christmas by which
everyone had thought it would all be over in that now
distant summer of 1914.

Bill looked up at the sound of a Blériot spotter plane far
above. He was just in time to see the tiny black cross of
fuselage and wings vanish into a towering snow-laden
cloud. The artillery barrage in the distance stirred the pools
of water, too oily to freeze, with tiny ripples like the echoes
of a distant earthquake. He leaned on the trench wall and
reached for his cigarettes. He unwrapped the scrap of wax-
cloth that kept the precious matches dry and struck one on
the tins of bully beef embedded in the trench wall to stop it
collapsing. Shielding the already half-smoked dog-end
from the chilly wind, he drew thankfully on the dry
tobacco. Smoke from a burning farmhouse drifted across
the high, cold December sky and the tip of the crushed
cigarette glowed briefly, a tiny fire in the dim earthy pit.
Beyond the parapet above his head a barren greyness full of
holes and ice stretched like a carpet of broken mirrors,
pierced with barbed wire and rotting wood. On the horizon
towards the German trenches, a line of trees that had been a
favourite spot for picnics before the war stood shattered
and stark, enormous sticks of charcoal in the bleak, failing

light. Like wandering ghosts, tiny flurries of snow danced across no-man's-land and settled on the helmets and the shoulders of the fallen as night came down. 'Some bloody Christmas Eve,' he muttered as he shuffled down the narrow earthy way towards his dugout.

The section of trench held by the 6th Glasgow Battalion of the Territorial Army, 'Harry Lauder's Own', and the 15th H.L.I., recruited from the depots of Glasgow Corporation Transport – the 'Tramways Battalion' – was like any other, no better, no worse, no good. Somehow night was less bearable as thoughts of home crowded into the great black space that hung before the soldiers' eyes. Men lay or half-sat in their primitive lean-tos, remembering hours and minutes in a world where there was no war.

At 11.30 p.m. Bill stirred uncomfortably, unable to settle down. He felt as if his feet had fallen off. 'Sandy? Are ye therr?' he asked, peering into the gloom.

'Aye?' said Sandy, with the clarity of a man wide-awake in the dark. 'Where do you think I am, Bill? Drivin' a Number 23 tram to Baillieston?'

'Ye wish,' his mate replied lugubriously.

An irate face poked in through the gap in the groundsheet covering the lean-to. 'Get that light out,' Sergeant Thomson bawled.

'It's not a light, S'jint,' Sandy replied quickly. 'It's the moon, S'jint!'

'I don't care what the adjective thing is, pit it OOT!' the sergeant shouted, withdrawing his head. He smacked the cloth wall with his stick and moved off down the line. 'Lights out!' he yelled, and men groaned and muttered as his voice grew fainter, finally rounding the corner into another 'street'.

'Right you are, S'jint!' Sandy shouted after him as soon as he was sure the man was out of earshot.

'You'd better shut up,' Bill cautioned him. 'Ye'll get done for dumb insolence or somethin'.'

'I'm no dumb,' Sandy replied vehemently.

'All right, all right,' Bill said. 'Just tellin' ye, that's all.'

'Know what time it is in there?' echoed the sergeant's voice faintly as he crossed an intersection down the line.

'Aye, S'jint, three bags full, S'jint,' said Sandy with derision. 'It's Christmas Eve, that's what time it is.'

They lay there in the dark, listening to the muted coughs and grunts of the men on either side of them.

'Sandy!' Bill hissed.

'What is it?' Sandy replied sleepily.

'Listen!' Bill said again.

'What tae?' Sandy asked. 'There's nuthin' to listen tae!'

'That's just it,' Bill replied, standing up and banging his head. 'Nothin'. The artillery's stopped firin'.'

Sandy sat up in the dark. 'There's something going on outside,' he said, puzzled. 'There's voices.'

Outside the trench was full of men standing about or shuffling past each other. A party had come back along the 'corduroy' after fatigues in the ruined wood nearby, and it seemed something strange was going on near the 'Alleyman' trenches, but nobody seemed to know exactly what.

'This is helluva'n odd, this,' Bill said as he and Sandy made their way among their comrades. 'I think the hale battalion's out here just lookin'.'

'And what for?' Sandy asked. 'There's nothin' to . . .'

'Listen!' Bill whispered urgently, interrupting him. 'Kin you hear . . . singin'?'

Far away across the broken lands a man was singing in a high clear voice. There is nothing more terrible, or more beautiful, than sound where there should never be any again, like crying from inside the coffin when the lid's tight shut. The clear notes echoed across the ruined countryside.

> *Stille nacht, Heilige nacht,*
> *Alles schläft, einsam wacht . . .*

'In the name o' the wee man,' Bill said, turning to his mate in amazement. 'I know that wan. "Still the night".' He began to hum the tune. 'I remember learning it in Miller Street Primary when I was wee.' Men were climbing up and peering over the edge of the trench. Bill joined them. 'There's a light over the Jerry lines,' he said.

'Watch yersel',' Sandy urged, pulling at his greatcoat. 'It's likely a night attack or somethin'.'

'Naw, naw, I don't think so,' Bill replied. 'Here! The light's oan top of a stick, or a rifle or somethin'.'

All around them men were clambering over the parapet and staring across no-man's-land. Bill pulled himself up beside them and looked towards the enemy. Sandy scrambled after his friend and they stood together with the rest of the battalion until, one by one, they began to walk slowly towards the German trenches.

'This is daft,' Sandy said anxiously.

Bill turned and looked at him. 'Naw. Come on. I've got to see this.'

'Well, all right then,' Sandy replied doubtfully. 'I'm right behind you. I'll no' let them get ye, Bill.'

Halfway across Bill and Sandy stopped. Someone had brought along a 'moothie', and had begun to play what was supposed to be a Christmas carol.

'Look!' Bill said, pointing. 'Mair lights in the Jerry trenches.'

'No' jist that,' Sandy gasped. 'Germans. Comin' towards us!'

'There's bloody hundreds of them,' said a soldier in a kilt beside them.

A party of *Feldgrauen*, carrying a rather scrawny Christmas tree, marched towards them in close order. They stopped about ten yards away from the Scots, tried to stick the tree in the frozen ground, succeeded, and stood back, looking at their handiwork. With comic slowness, the Christmas tree toppled over and lay in between the two groups. It was obviously a branch rather than a tree, but in the flickering light that the lanterns cast on the blackened, freezing earth, it was very green.

'I've left my rifle,' Sandy said in sudden panic. 'I'll get court-martialled.'

'Then the hale army'll get court-martialled,' replied Bill curtly. 'Shut up. Here's that big yin comin'.'

The tall officer in the grey overcoat walked towards them, arms outstretched, the snow making the spike on the top of his helmet look like a damp candle. He paused beside the fallen Christmas tree, looked up, and smiled.

Suddenly they were all smiling and laughing.

'Is he high up, dae ye think, Bill?' Sandy asked.

'See those green lanyards and tassels on his shoulders? They're sniper's cords. He's a Proosian,' Bill replied, staring in fascination as the man strode towards him.

'That's the first German I've ever seen,' Sandy said.

'Me too,' his mate muttered, blowing on his fingers.

'*Unglaublich!*' the officer said. '*Prächtiger Kerl!*'

'Er . . . dae ye no speak English?' Bill asked uncertainly.

The Prussian smiled. '*Ja! Ja!*' he said warmly. 'Good Merry Christmas. I am wishing you both Season's Greetings from Germany. I was in your country, England, before the war.'

'Now haud on!' said Sandy, stepping forward. 'Compliments of the Season and aw' that, but we're Scottish.'

'Frae Glesca',' said Bill offering the man a cigarette.

The man paused thoughtfully. 'Glasgow,' he said, stroking his moustache. 'I was study in Glasgow two years before . . .' he left the sentence unfinished.

'Aye, yer right, pal. Before!' Bill agreed. 'Put it there!' He held out his mittened hand.

The German took it. 'How are you called?' he asked.

'I'm Bill, and this here is my mate Sandy,' Bill grinned.

The German took the cigarette and stuck it in the corner of his mouth. 'Ach so! Hello, Beel!' he said, taking it out again. He turned round, calling to the men standing in the shadows beyond the fallen tree, '*Dieter, Willy! Kommt her!*'

'Listen, big yin,' Bill said, hunting for his matches. 'I don't know how long this is going to last, but let's mak' the maist of it!'

'Mak' the maist of it?' echoed the German slowly. 'Ah yes,' he nodded, 'Make the most of it, but "big yin"? Was ist "big yin"?'

113

STRIKE!

The Great War was over, and Russia and Germany were in chaos. The Kaiser had escaped to Holland to grow cabbages, and in St. Petersburg the marble palaces echoed to the tramp of Red Guards as Vladimir Ilyich Lenin addressed workers' and soldiers' soviets. In Britain huge numbers of soldiers were being demobbed, and by the end of 1919 over four million men had returned to 'civvy street'. The war had driven prices up by 125 per cent since 1914, and it rapidly became clear that nothing was ever going to be the same again. The industrial unrest that had been coming to a head in August 1914 now re-asserted itself in the campaign for a shorter working week. Trade Union membership had risen from four million before the war to over eight million, and in Glasgow it was clear that confrontation was imminent.

The gas-lamps in the streets beside Cowlairs Works made yellow circles in the fog. The soldiers had been unloading tanks all day, and in the strike-bound silence the rattle of chains and couplings and the roar of powerful diesel engines could be heard right across Springburn.

The damp seemed to be in the process of amputating Private Enderby's toes as he stamped up and down beside the buffers. Enderby had been unloading the cumbersome vehicles since two that afternoon, and now, eight hours later, he was tired, chilled to the bone, and more than a little sick of the whole business.

The driver braked his left-hand track to turn the vehicle and edge it slowly down the makeshift ramp from the railway wagon to the ground.

'Back!' Enderby bawled. 'That's it! More to your right!'

The tracks of the Mark V bit deep into the damp wood

and rusty steel of the ramp. The front hatch lay open as the tank commander peered down into the fog, relaying the private's instruction to the gearman and the brakeman inside. Normally carrying a crew of six, the undermanned juggernaut lurched forward. The vibration, noise, smell and heat were incredible, and the man down below looked up nervously at the metal giant roaring and towering above him. Wood began to splinter and crack. 'Back again! Stop!' he yelled, with the desperation of a man shouting at an earthquake. 'Back! STOP!'

The vehicle lurched to one side and hung there, the caterpillar tracks along one side churning the air uselessly.

'Blimey! That's torn it!' Enderby said under his breath.

Stepping carefully across the tracks, Colonel Withers stamped up to him and glared. 'You blithering idiot!' he shouted. 'Don't you know how to give signals?'

'S ... sorry, sir,' Enderby stammered. 'It's the fog.'

'I've a good mind to put you on a charge,' the Colonel fumed.

The tank commander clambered down the side of his machine and joined them. 'You know I drove her through a post office at Bullecourt,' he said sadly. 'Not a mark on her. And here she is stuck on a railway siding in Blighty.'

'Well, it's a right "Mesapolinica",' replied the Colonel, looking at the tank, still shaking and struggling like an enormous beetle stranded on its back. He turned to Private Enderby. 'Do you think I like it here, man?'

'Dunno, sir,' the Private replied damply.

'Well I don't,' Colonel Withers answered. 'I'd rather be at home with my family, instead of up here in God knows where.'

'Glasgow, sir,' the Private supplied helpfully.

'I know that, dammit!' the Colonel retorted crossly. 'Are you trying to be clever with me, young feller-me-lad? Well, just don't. 'Cause I'm a few pips cleverer than you, see. This lot's to be ready for the road by the Ack Emma, and that's not going to happen if we spend our time driving them off sideways.' He sneezed violently. 'November in Glasgow,' he said thickly, extracting a khaki handkerchief from his leather glove. 'Just look at it! Fog, fog, and more adjectival fog. If this is Scotland, I don't think much of it. I thought it was all mountains and heather.'

'I understand this is Spring Burn or somethin', sir,' Private Enderby said.

'Oh it is, is it?' the Colonel rounded on him. 'And where's that when it's at home?'

'North of Glasgow, sir,' came the reply.

The Colonel snorted and looked at the featureless wall of grey around them. 'Well, I don't mind telling you, Private,' he said. 'I'm sick of it already. Might as well be Funky Villas or Jolly Polly or Liverpool for all I can see. "Supervise unloading tanks, Glasgow" is the order. There could be ten thousand here for all I can make out.'

'There's about forty on the siding,' Private Enderby informed him. 'All Mark V's, except for the VIII up by the football park.'

'What blithering idiot despatched a Mark VIII?' spluttered the Colonel. 'There only are four and the damn thing weighs thirty-seven tons.'

'I know, sir,' agreed Private Enderby. 'It's bogged down.'

'Bogged down in Glasgow,' said the Colonel fatalistically. 'Let's see if we can find the others, man.' He shivered. 'No wonder half of Europe's down with Spanish Influenza when the weather's as rotten as this.'

Muted roarings could be heard coming from beyond the signal box.

'Now, what the devil's all that?' asked Colonel Withers.

'Must be the others,' Enderby said quietly.

'Well let's get them down then,' the Colonel snapped, squaring his shoulders, 'or I'll have to carry the can. We'll soon put the wind up these Glasgow Reds . . . soon sort em' out!' He strode off into the fog.

'Yes, sir,' said Private Enderby to himself, 'Sort them out, sir.'

The fraternal delegate from Tradeston thumped the table angrily. 'Let them bring their troops intae Glasgow!' he shouted defiantly. 'Then we'll see what happens ... tae them!'

Everyone tried to speak at once. The small smoky room was in an uproar. Manny Shinwell pushed back his chair and stood up. 'Comrades! Comrades!' he said loudly and firmly. The noise died down.

'Comrades,' he continued more quietly. 'Sir Robert Horne has refused to intervene on our behalf in spite of his "Glasgow" connection, so the rest is up to this Strike Committee. We have to help ourselves. I have also to report to the Committee that the tanks in Springburn are reported to be ready to come out and block the streets and knock down barricades, but it's my belief we have them on the run. This is a panic reaction by the authorities. It's them that's running scared. Now, the next thing to consider is the picket of the ...'

He was interrupted by the delegate from the North British Loco Works. 'That's all very well, Comrade Shinwell. What I say, through the Chair, is look at Russia, look at Red Rosa and the Spartacists in Berlin. If oor ain boys are for us, then we're away!'

'Away where?' Willy Gallacher asked. 'I'd be with you if I thought fighting the Army was the way to a shorter working week, but it's no'!'

The delegate turned to him and shook his head. 'No, no, comrade,' he said. 'Trotsky says: "Hesitation is to be regarded as treason to the revolution."'

'What "treason" and what "revolution"?' Gallacher said, leaning forward.

The room became very quiet.

'I'm no' talking about fighting the soldiers, Willy,' the man said hastily.

'What are you talking about then?' Willy Gallacher asked.

The delegate stood up. 'Comrades!' he said, 'If the soldiers are on our side, if the boys are with us, then we are talking about workers' and soldiers' soviets.'

'That's a big "if",' Manny Shinwell replied. 'It may come to that and it may not, but for now the strike's solid.'

The delegates on either side of him applauded. 'And the mass meeting in George Square goes ahead.'

'Right then!' said Willy Gallacher. 'Anything else?'

'Aye!' said the delegate from Tradeston, putting up his hand. 'Through the Chair of course.'

'On ye go,' Willy Gallacher sighed.

'Er . . . er, the strike goes on,' said the man.

'We just said that,' Shinwell replied. 'But your point's noted, Comrade, through the Chair of course.'

George Square was a sea of caps and headscarves. A lorry stood outside the City Chambers and from the back of it members of the Strike Committee and others addressed the vast crowd. On the fringe of the mass of people, Privates Higgs and Putnam, only two of the hundreds of soldiers deployed less than discreetly round the square, had orders to fix bayonets on receiving the signal. As they watched they could just make out the statue of Robert Burns, daisy in hand, poking his head above the thousands more familiar with his name than the words of the song they were trying to sing. The ragged strains of the 'Internationale' surged across the square.

'We'll need the Linseed Lancers if this lot turn nasty,' said Alf Higgs, a hint of fear in his voice.

'Blimey!' gasped Private Putnam. 'Cop that, mate!'

Across the square by the lorry the Red Flag had been hoisted and the singing had intensified. Without warning, mounted police charged into the Square from the side streets, supported by baton-swinging special constables. A great roar went up from the crowd, a mixture of anger and despair.

'Ever wish yer was back in France, Dick?' asked Alf Higgs, stepping back into a doorway.

'Blimey! Anywhere,' replied Dick. 'I'd rather be facing Jerry than Red Clydeside any day of the week.'

NO MEAN GANGS

It was the early 1930s, the years of the 'Norman Conks', the 'Billy Boys', the 'Maryhill Fleet', the 'Southside Stickers' and a host of other clans, tribes, sub-septs and lone psychopaths, who together wrote the legend of Glasgow's gangland in blood and broken bottles.

The city's police looked on doubtfully when Yorkshireman Captain Percy Sillitoe arrived as the new Chief Constable with his 'new broom', but Sillitoe eventually became the terror of the gangsters of Glasgow. He went to Chicago and met J. Edgar Hoover and Elliot Ness, and when he came back to Scotland, his new 'flying squad' of radio cars, the first in Britain, put out the call-sign that spelled the death of mob terror and gangland violence in Glasgow. But it was a war of many battles, and some defeats, before the spirit of the gangs was finally broken.

One Sunday morning early in 1932 a group of men stood lounging on the corner of Norman Street and Finnart Street, white scarves tucked into their open-necked shirts, hair slicked back with margarine. Someone made a joke.

The tall man at the centre of the group smiled briefly, the livid white scar on his face curving into a sinister 'S'. 'That wis a good wan that, Frenchie,' he said.

'I thought ye'd like that, Bull,' Frenchie said sycophantically. 'An' when she says to him . . .'

'Aye, aye, that's fine. We heard ye the first time.'

'Whatever ye say, Bull,' replied Frenchie, cowed.

'Aye, yer right,' Bull Bowman grinned mirthlessly. 'Whatever I say.'

They both turned as they heard the sound of running feet coming towards them along the litter-strewn pavement. 'Here's the wee Scud man comin', Bull,' Frenchie said.

'Ah kin see that,' Bull replied squaring his shoulders.

'Wife been giein' ye a doin' again?' Frenchie quipped as the wee man drew level with them.

'Naw, naw, Frenchie,' he gasped. 'It's the Billy Boys!'

Bull Bowman took hold of his lapels and lifted him bodily off the ground. 'What wis that?' he growled.

'Honest, Bull,' squealed Scud. 'It wisny me!'

Bull dropped him the way a child drops somebody else's toy. 'Where's ma lookouts?' he said threateningly to Frenchie. 'See if you're havin' me oan, Scud, I'll carve ye from buttonhole tae breakfast, so ah wull.'

'I'm no', Bull,' Scud whimpered. 'They're jist comin' up Abercrombie Street the noo!'

'Right then,' said Bowman in a voice of command, 'Frenchie?'

'Here, Bull,' answered the loyal Frenchie, stating the obvious. He adjusted his cravat, ready for the honour of orders from the homicidal maniac he called his friend.

'You've tae get the reinforcements,' Bull said. 'They'll be up at Olympia Street.'

'You mean at Gilmour's Club?' Frenchie asked him.

'Naw, the Olympic Games in Italy,' his leader replied sarcastically. 'Get oan yer wey, ya lug-face!'

'Aye Bull, I wull Bull,' Frenchie assured him, running off like a rabbit pursued by a greyhound. 'I'm oan ma way, Bull,' he shouted, vanishing round the corner.

Bull Bowman stared at his carefully-manicured fingernails. 'I'm gaun' tae blooter that Fullarton,' he said quietly. 'It's about time the Norman Conks sorted out the Billy Boys wance and for all. Are ye all right ma darlins?' He opened his jacket and looked down affectionately at the white handles of the two cutthroat razors open and ready in each of the breast pockets of his waistcoat.

'Aye, and ye kin and all, Bull,' said the forgotten Scud. 'You're the chief, so ye are.'

Bowman turned and looked at him with eyes that glittered with malice. 'Shut it, you!' he ordered. 'What are you still here for, eh? Rin up tae ma house and get ma pick handle.'

'The new wan?' asked Scud doubtfully.

'They're all new,' Bowman laughed. 'Ask the wumman for the axe under the box-bed mattress and aw'.'

Although the leaders of both gangs were arrested as a result of the battle that raged that day in Abercrombie Street, the derisory fines they received were soon paid after the customary 'levy' on local shopkeepers. As the years passed in violence and feuding, Commander Sillitoe became ever more determined to fight fire with fire, and after his mounted police – 'Sillitoe's Cossacks' – ambushed the Billy Boys in 1935, only Bowman's rival, the boastful and murderous William Fullarton, remained at large.

The gang of neds and girls strolled up the street, laughing drunkenly. The shiny black peak of a cap and the hint of a black and white check, 'Sillitoe's Tartan', appeared round the wall of a wash-house, then was quickly withdrawn.

'You did the right thing, lad,' said Constable Morrison, his enormous bulk wedged neatly in the concrete doorway. 'That's Fullarton right enough.'

'Do you want me to go for help?' asked the young bobby.

'Why?' asked Morrison. 'Do you need help? I don't.'

'There's about twenty of them, Constable Morrison,' the young man said nervously. 'And only two of us.'

'More's the pity for them then,' Morrison grinned. He looked round the corner again. 'Right enough. Fullarton,' he said with glee. 'He's struttin' about there as if we'd never broken up the gang at all. He's got a wee lassie with him, looks like Chopper MacKay's daughter, and if there's trouble, the wee kiddie's as good as deid. Now, lad, it's about five hundred yards to the station down the road, so off we go and huckle him. What are you waiting for?'

'Er . . . what's the charge?' the young policeman asked.

'Oh, I'll think of something,' Morrison replied. He marched up to the rabble in the street, the young constable beside him looking as stern and brave as his twenty years would allow. 'Right then, Fullarton!' he said loudly. 'What's all this then?'

The gang stopped their horseplay and looked at the two men in amazement.

'Haw, haw!' laughed the drunken Fullarton. 'Look at this, lads. It's Big Tommy frae the Toll. Want a carry, son?'

'Constable Morrison or Big Tommy, it's all one,' said the policeman with a frown. 'This is the law talking to you, and Chief Constable Sillitoe and all.'

'Silly-toe? Where is he then?' asked Fullarton, staggering slightly. 'Get yer dukes up then. I don't see no Silly-toe.'

'Aye, well, you can see this!' Morrison shouted, drawing his baton. 'Fullarton!' Big Tommy roared. 'I arrest you for being drunk in charge of a child!'

Fullarton looked at him stupidly for a moment, grinned in disbelief, and handed the child to one of the women. 'Get them, lads!' he shouted, and the neds charged at the two policemen.

Like a bulldog with a ferret, Morrison reached out with a huge hand and took hold of Fullarton by the neck, keeping him at arm's length.

'Leave us,' the mobster choked, his fists flailing at the empty air.

'What you going to do?' asked Big Tommy. 'Send for the polis?' With his free hand he whacked a couple of heads that had come within range, and saw with approval that the young bobby was having little difficulty fending off his attackers, standing as he was with his back to the mighty Morrison.

'They've goat the king!' somebody shouted before a large fist sent him to an early retirement on the pavement. Two more of Fullarton's 'braves' limped out of range of the human tank.

'Come oan! Help us, well!' gurgled Fullarton, still in the vice-like grip of the policeman's hand.

The neds hung back uncertainly.

'Yer all yella,' screamed Fullarton, struggling like a rabbit in a snare.

'I'm taking your "king" in,' said Morrison firmly, 'me and my colleague here, so ye've all had it! The Billy Boys are finished, and the Norman Conks and all. Ye hear? Finished! The whole hand-picked midden of heid-bangers.'

Holding Fullarton between them, the two constables frogmarched their charge towards the police station. With a final despairing howl the 'king' of the Billy Boys was dragged up the steps and into oblivion.

The terrible 'Knuckles' Williamson sat in his single-end in Bridgeton nursing a black eye and what felt like a broken arm. His long-suffering wife Isa had never seen the confirmed hard man in such a state. 'So that's it,' she said. 'Fullarton's inside.'

'Aye,' he moaned. 'But it was terrible so it wis, Isa. I ran after Billy and then . . . then Big Tommy from the Toll hit me, and everything went dark, so it did.'

'Ah well, ye've had a good run,' she replied. 'Ye'll have a bit more time now.'

'Whit fur?' Knuckles winced.

'There's a few things needin' done about the place.' She sat down and looked at the shattered wreck at the other side of the table.

'Dae I have to?' he asked despairingly.

'Aye, ye dae,' she said firmly. 'And because ye want to. This is a home, no' a prison.'

'Yes dear,' he said, looking at her with one eye.

So the Glasgow gangs vanished from the pages of the local press and passed into history, but the years of the razor kings still cast a chilling shadow across the remaining tenements and back-courts, and an unexpected shout on a frosty night can bring back memories of sudden death in the streets.

THE NIGHT CLYDEBANK WOULDN'T DIE

The thirteenth of March 1941 had been a glorious spring day in Clydebank. New grass and green buds lined the banks of the canal, and the Campsies, grey and purple in the distance, held warmer shadows in their tumbled folds and ridges. The evening sun lit up the windows of the Holy City, flashing with a pale fire that could be seen all the way across the Clyde Valley in Paisley. A tiny Number 20 single-decker tram rattled over the swing bridge at Kilbowie Road, and the cranes and half-finished hulls in Brown's beyond the Town Hall cast lengthening shadows on the road to Dalmuir. It was almost nine o'clock, and outside the Seven Seas knots of men stood on the pavement chatting before turning for home. The great clock in Singer's Yard struck the hour; and like the first flicker of a nightmare, the banshee wail of the sirens and the approaching drone of the Heinkel 111s and Junkers 88s of the Luftwaffe began together.

The harsh light of the naked yellow bulbs flooded the underground Control Centre beneath Clydebank Public Library. Ever since the first incendiaries had fallen near the ambulance shelter in Singer's Yard, reports had been flooding in and every telephone in the place was ringing.

Town Clerk Henry Kelly anxiously glanced at the map on the wall. 'Are you sure, Bill?' he asked.

'I'm telling you, Henry,' William Thomson, his deputy, replied. 'Singer's wood yard's ablaze and the fifteen-inch water main in Kilbowie Road's been hit. There's no water to fight the fire.'

'The water will be coming out like Niagara Falls, so they can maybe use the crater as it fills up,' Henry answered.

A young girl handed him some slips of paper and hurried

off again. 'Listen to this!' the Town Clerk said. 'Livingstone Street all ablaze, Agamemnon Street, Jellicoe Street, Pattison Street ...' He leafed through the remainder quickly. 'The whole of Clydebank's on fire.'

The ceiling shook and plaster fell like snow, making the two men look suddenly grey. The lights flickered, dimmed, and then came on again. Someone started lighting candles. Like drumbeats in a cellar, the sound of high explosives shattering the packed tenements vibrated through the reinforced walls of the Control Centre.

Henry Kelly turned again to the map on the wall. 'Now, Bill,' he said, 'Janet Hyslop, the Head Warden of E Group, says that Second Terrace and the ...'

He was interrupted as a girl ran up to him. 'Mr. Kelly! Mr. Kelly!'

'Yes, Jean,' he replied. 'Try and be calm now, dear.'

The girl burst into tears. 'I've just heard,' she sobbed. 'The tenements up in Livingstone Street ... My mother lives up there.'

'Now, Jean,' he replied, calm but firm. 'We've got to keep a hold on things, for everybody's sake.' Fumbling in his pocket, he offered her a large crumpled handkerchief.

Jean blew her nose loudly and copiously.

'Now, dear,' he said reassuringly, 'Let's have a wee look at the map. Livingstone Street, you said? Now that's maybe unexploded. You've not to worry. The main thing is to keep the information coming in and going out, for all our sakes. Do you understand?'

'Yes. I'm sorry, Mr. Kelly,' she replied, sniffling.

'There's a brave girl then. On you go.' Henry sighed. 'I wish someone would say "It's all right" to me, Bill.'

Before Bill Thomson could reply there was an enormous crash. The entire building shook, the lights winked out and the room was plunged into blackness.

'Get that emergency generator going!' Henry Kelly shouted into the darkness.

'That's a direct hit on the Library upstairs,' said Bill somewhere beside him.

With a deep-throated roar the generator came on and the

lights flickered on again. The ceiling above was intact, but some ominous cracks had appeared.

'I'd better get the C.D. War Room in Glasgow,' Kelly said, picking up the telephone. 'Hello? Switchboard? Hello?' He put the receiver down angrily. 'Damn!' he muttered. 'It's dead. Any phones on?' he called out.

'They're all dead, Mr. Kelly,' someone shouted back.

'Well listen, everyone,' he said loudly, standing up. 'We're all right, and that's what matters. We still have a job to do. Carry on with your work, dust off the papers and sharpen your pencils. The cleaners are going to have some job in the morning.'

He was greeted with nervous laughter and the tension in the beleaguered cellar lessened a little. The sound of explosions could still be heard in the distance.

'Carry on!' Kelly said, sitting down again. 'That's all we can do, Bill. There are the runners standing by in case something like this happened. And send word to the Police that we need their radio . . . NOW!'

'If the polis station is still there,' Bill replied, picking up the list of couriers from the desk. He walked across to the far wall, opened the blast doors and looked up towards the waste ground at the back of the Library. A rapid succession of bangs, like balloons bursting in the distance, was followed by an enormous sliding roar somewhere near at hand. Bill closed the door, dogged it, and came back again.

'What's it like up there?' asked Henry Kelly, not really wanting to know.

'I thought it was the dawn for a minute,' his friend said quietly. 'The sky at the top of the stairs is bright red.'

'The dawn's a long way off,' replied Henry Kelly, brushing the plaster dust off his shoulders.

The gates to Singer's wood yard stood open. One of them leaned crazily to one side, its hinges twisted and shattered. Charlie Anderson, his hair singed and his shirt sticking to his back with sweat, struggled with the pump he was trying to connect to the hose that snaked off into the giant crater that had smashed Kilbowie Road in half.

'You'll have to leave it, Anderson!' Jimmy Aird shouted, running up to him as specks of soot filled the air like black snow.

'I'm no' deef!' Anderson replied, his fingers bleeding where he had tried to force the brass connector on the hose onto the pump. 'What's that smell?' he asked. 'Smells like beer.'

'You're no' wrang!' Jimmy Aird shouted above the din of collapsing tenements and the crackle of flames. 'Yoker Distillery's got it. The Yoker Bar and all,' he added sadly. 'But come away, Charlie. Ye canna stay here. The heat aff the yard'll fry ye, man!'

Charlie Anderson straightened up painfully. He was still wearing his carpet slippers. He had been pressing his trousers for the bowling club meeting the next day when the raid started and the right leg still showed a sharp, neat crease. The left leg looked as though it had been mangled by a combine harvester.

'There's nothin' more ye can do here,' Jimmy urged, pulling at his elbow.

An incendiary went off on the roof of the sten-gun plant in Singer's and an enormous bundle of planks slid in flames, to smash onto the ground nearby.

'It's like Hell with the lid off,' Jimmy said, wide-eyed.

'Ye have to do something,' Charlie replied. His hair stood up on end, stiff and brittle as straw. 'Ye canna take it in. I never thought it would be like this.'

'Leave it. It'll have to burn out,' bawled Jimmy over the ear-splitting bangs of high-explosive. 'And that's not just the brewery ye can smell. There's a gas main away somewhere. Come on! They need a hand in Pattison Street.'

'All right then,' said Charlie in a dazed voice.

The two men ran into Pattison Street. The tenements towered up on either side like a stage set, each window lit by red from behind. Suddenly Jimmy pushed his friend roughly to the ground. Inches away, the parapet of a building struck the pavement with skull-shattering force.

'My God!' said Charlie, struggling to his feet. 'There's a

hand sticking out of thae bricks!'

'Well, don't just stand there,' Jimmy coughed as smoke drifted up the street towards them. 'Help us!'

They tore frantically at the rubble, unaware of the blood that streamed from their fingers, staining the red sandstone black.

'It's a wumman!' Charlie gasped, cradling her head in his hand. 'She's still alive. Where's thon ambulance?'

'Somewhere else,' Jimmy replied, clearing a pile of bricks from her shins. 'There now,' he said as the woman opened her eyes weakly. 'Yer goin' to be all right, dear.'

'Where's Morag?' she whispered.

'Who's Morag?' Charlie asked gently.

'She's . . . she's my daughter, my wee lassie,' the woman said with difficulty.

Jimmy looked up and frowned. 'She's in a bad way, Charlie,' he mouthed. 'We'll need to get help.'

Charlie looked up at the flames dancing on the rooftops of the Holy City and the searchlights criss-crossing the rosy sky like white needles. A few ack-ack shells burst overhead, flowering briefly under the belly of the clouds, but bombs continued to rain down on the virtually defenceless town. 'Where are we to get help from?' he asked blankly. 'There's nuthin' left.'

'This is no' war,' Jimmy said, his shoulders bowed. 'It's murder.'

Charlie smiled, the way men sometimes do when facing unbelievable odds. 'Whatever it is,' he said. 'I'm alive, you're alive, and we've to do something for the wifie here. Come on, man, dig! Use yer hands, Jim.'

Jimmy looked down at his fingers in sudden realization. 'I've cut masel',' he said bleakly. 'I'm bleedin'.'

'So's Clydebank,' replied Charlie Anderson. 'Keep goin'.'

LAND OF THE LOBBY DOSSERS

At the end of the Second World War, with much of Europe in ruins, life at home remained harsh and full of shortages. The black market flourished and ration books were still the order of the day. Everything was earmarked for export and for a time it seemed that one of the major exports was the 'G.I. Bride'. Fruit and meat, clothes, paper and a hundred other items were almost unobtainable. In 1947, the year of Frank Sinatra's 'Five Minutes More', the bread ration was cut again, and tuberculosis was still the scourge of Glasgow. With tension growing between the former allies of East and West and an 'Iron Curtain' descending over Europe, there were power shortages and coal stocks were running low. Scotland found itself in the grip of the worst winter in living memory, and to cap it all, the postwar housing problem had reached crisis proportions. Years of war and neglect, coupled with the demob of hundreds of thousands of soldiers, had only made matters worse in the already overcrowded city. Many people, relatives and lodgers alike, slept in what were virtually cupboards or hallways, and Glasgow became the land of the 'lobby dossers'.

Gorbals Cross was crowded with traffic. Buses and trams stretching back towards Victoria Bridge met traffic coming along Ballater Street, and people threaded their way in and out of the stalled vehicles or sat on the top decks of the 'bone-shakers' and read their *Citizen* or *Times* or drummed their fingers impatiently on the seat in front. It was near Christmas and the lights from the pubs and the sweetie shops, the jenny-a'-things and the cafés were reflected on the wet cobblestones and the puddles between the tramlines snaking down the middle of the streets. People hunched their shoulders and hurried along, the collars of their coats turned up, umbrellas bobbing up and down like a procession of giant beetles on either side of the road. Someone with a relative in Canada had put up a Christmas tree with fairy lights in the window and the tiny red and green and yellow bulbs winked on and off in defiance of power cuts, shortages, and the raw, bitter sleet, already turning to snow.

Round the corner at No. 19 St. Ninian Street things were no less hectic. Mrs. McMenemy had been out doing some late shopping. It was hard enough having to wait outside the butcher or the Co-op for a wee bit of mince or whale meat or whatever was on offer at the time, but with her man Bobby on shifts at the yard and the boys back, bringing their friends with them, she hardly had any time for anything any more. As she reached the first landing Mrs. Sinclair's door opened and her neighbour came out, her pinny attached to the front of her cardigan by a single large safety-pin. She was holding a stack of newsprint neatly cut up into squares and threaded on a string.

'Needin' mair toilet paper, Isa?' Mrs. McMenemy enquired politely.

'Aye, well seein' it's no rationed, Sadie,' Isa Sinclair smiled, unlocking the narrow door of the communal toilet and going inside.

'Maybe see you later!' Sadie McMenemy said loudly as she started to climb the next flight of stairs.

'Very good then, Sadie!' Isa replied.

Arriving at her own landing, Sadie put her shopping bag down with a sigh and turned the key in the lock thankfully.

The way into the hall was barred by an upturned bicycle frame.

'For heaven's sake, John!' she said crossly. 'Can ye no' do your bike somewhere else?'

John Yule put down his puncture kit and looked up in surprise. 'Sorry Mrs. McMenemy,' he said. 'I didn't expect you back for a while.'

'It is ma' hoose,' she replied coldly, stepping over the bits and pieces spread out in the hall. 'How can I get in and out to my shopping or take the pram with the bag wash out to the steamie with kit-bags, blankets, bikes and the hale jing-bang cluttering up my lobby? There's half of Glasgow bidin' in this hoose, so there is.'

'Let me get the door for you,' he said anxiously, squeezing past her.

'Thanks, son,' she replied grudgingly, flattening herself against the gas meter.

John reached the door, tripped over the dynamo he had been attempting to repair and sent a string of milk bottles crashing down the stairs. 'I ... I'm sorry, Mrs. McMenemy,' he stammered in embarrassment.

'So am I, son. It's no' as if we were doon at the close. This is three sterrs up, and it's no' ma turn to mop them doon. There's broken glass all the way down to the next landing. Ma wee cat will get slashed tae ribbons.'

'I'll clean it up for you, honest,' he replied quickly. 'Then I'll be going out of your road for a while.'

'Aye, well,' she said, slightly mollified. 'See that you do, son. I've enough on my plate having to wash and cook for five without all that mess.'

John went out onto the landing and began to pick up the broken glass.

'You are a right pair,' she called after him. 'You and that son of mine. How you beat the Germans, the pair of ye, when you canna fix punctures and that, I don't know.'

'There you are,' he said, stepping back in over the bike. 'I think that's the lot.'

'Och, put it down in the corner there a minute,' she frowned. 'You've cut yourself!'

'It's nothing, really.' John put the glass down carefully and sucked his finger.

'Come on now.' She put her hand on his maternally. 'You don't have to be a hero with me. I'm old enough to be your mammy. Let's see.'

He winced with pain.

'It's bad, son,' she said in a worried voice. 'Ye'll maybe need a stitch in it.'

John looked at the gash in his finger unhappily. 'But I'm

skint, Mrs. McMenemy,' he said. 'And I don't start work at the building till Monday.'

'Well you'll need to wash it.' Mrs. McMenemy nipped the edges of the angry wound together and John grimaced again. 'That Bevan's talkin' about free doctors, but it's no' happened yet. I think there's some sticking plaster in the tea caddy along with the clothing coupons.'

'It's just the thing though, isn't it?' he complained. 'March, two year ago, me and your Billy crossed the Rhine wi' Monty and captured Wesel, and he saved me from the Jerry sniper at the Henschel trainworks like I wis tellin' you. Both of us all through the Second World War without a scratch and here I am back in Glasgow and I get wounded in the Gorbals.'

'C'mon and not be silly,' she said, smiling. 'We'll get thon tea caddy. The sooner you start work, son, the better for ye. Oh, and when you do, I hope you'll be taking your bike with you.'

'I will, Mrs. McMenemy,' said the victor of Luneberg Heath, following her meekly. 'If I can get it fixed.'

Bobby McMenemy liked to go into the corner shop for some tobacco on his way home from the yard. As the shop-bell rang Mr. Rae looked up from sorting his papers and nodded. 'Aye, Mr. McMenemy,' he said. 'And how are you gettin' on the night?'

'Just gie's ma thick black and ma *Times* and I'll be on ma way,' McMenemy replied morosely.

'Do I detect a note of "life's not being very good to me"?' grinned the newsagent. He was one of those infuriating people who refuse to be depressed by anything, and if someone had told him that Jamaica Street Bridge had just collapsed, his wife and granny been run over by a convoy of fish lorries, and his wee corner shop been devastated by a rogue elephant, he would merely have grinned and said, 'To be or no to be, get me pal?'

Bobby McMenemy was not such an optimist. 'Ye canna buy nothin' these days,' he said grimly. 'Coupons for clothes, coupons for this, that and the other. They'll be comin' out with coupons for the "other" any day now, not that it would matter tae me anyway. And as well as that, me and her's got half the H.L.I. dossin' in wir lobby. Gie's ma baccy and I'll away and see if I can smoke them out.' He deposited some coins on the counter and picked up his tobacco and the newspaper. 'T.T.F.N.' he called as he opened the door and walked out into the sleet.

'Cheerybye, well,' Mr. Rae replied with a grin.

Bobby McMenemy leaned into the wind and tried not to think about the melting snow running down inside his collar. As he turned the corner into St. Ninian Street the full blast of the gale met him and he stared hard at the pavement, walking straight into the bizarre figure that had stepped out of the close in front of him.

'Psst! Jimmy!' said the apparition, hunching its shoulders and twitching to one side.

'Are you talking to me, pal?' replied Bobby bleakly.

The stranger was dressed in wide trousers and a long loose jacket padded out at the shoulders, as if he had forgotten to take the coat hanger out. The broad-brimmed 'titfer' was pulled down over his face the way Bobby had seen Edward G. Robinson do in the films, and the narrow, pinched face was neatly divided by a thin black moustache that looked as though it might have been drawn on. 'Dae you fancy a wee present for the wife?' the spiv leered, leaning forward and attempting to wrap his shoulders around his ears.

'What's that?' asked Bobby, frowning. 'It's no' her birthday. What are you talkin' about? I'm just on my way hame from my work and I'm cold, wet and tired.'

'That's just it,' said the wide-boy with a knowing wink. 'I could tell ye were a family man the minute I clapped the old peepers on ye. "Backbone of the nation," I says to masel'. Now, what perks the little woman up at the end of the day?'

'Here! What are you gettin' at?' Bobby said aggressively.

With the flourish of a conjuror producing a ten-shilling note from a rabbit's ear, the spiv drew a piece of nondescript cloth from somewhere inside his tent-like jacket. 'What about that?' he hissed expectantly.

'What's aw' this?' asked Bobby, taken by surprise. 'Vests?'

The spiv looked hurt. 'Naw, naw, naw,' he said. 'But listen, I can see you are a connysewer of lingerie, and nae mistake. This here is finest quality shot silk frae . . . frae . . . Pekin'. That's right, Pekin'.'

Bobby looked at him sharply and stifled a sneeze. 'Listen pal,' he sighed. 'The hoose is full of lodgers, the wife's run off her feet, a man was tellin' me at work today that in the next war they'll be droppin' atom bombs on us. I've not had a very good day. Just leave us alane, will ye? I've nae time for lads in zoot suits, nor nighties off the back of a lorry neither.'

'Just private enterprise, sir,' the man said, taking a step back. 'That's what the war was all about.'

'Oh,' said Bobby, smiling. 'Soldier was ye? Where at? Germany? Africa?'

The man started to edge away. 'Oh, er . . . all over,' he replied evasively. 'I saw a lot of action, know what I mean?'

'Well in that case I know somebody that would love to talk to you,' Bobby said, taking a step towards him. 'Ma son and his pals just got their demob and they're dossin' down with us the now. Hang on and I'll send them down to see ye and talk over old times.'

The wide-boy turned and ran down the road with his jacket flapping around him. He looked like a drunken seagull trying to reach take-off speed as he vanished in the direction of Gorbals Cross.

'Here! Where are you off to?' Bobby shouted after him, laughing for the first time in weeks. 'Aye, run, ya spiv! My hoose may be choc-a-block full of lobby dossers, but they're all honest wans!'

The spiv had been in such a hurry he had dropped the 'shot Pekin' silk' on the pavement.

'This'll do for the boys to clean their bikes,' Bobby said, stooping to pick it up.

THE HOUSE THAT JIMMY BUILT

In 1950 the watchword was still 'austerity', and the countryside round Glasgow was soon to become built over with the largest housing schemes in Europe. It was the age of the pre-fab, a building technique largely pioneered in Glasgow. It had been found that something like 100,000 dwellings in Glasgow were either sub-standard or were in imminent danger of 'fallin' doon'. Many of these houses and flats had no hot water or proper sanitation, and 'sterrheid toilets' were sometimes used by as many as ten families. Glasgow Corporation, realizing the desperate need, had decided on a stupendous programme of municipal building at Ruchazie, Garthamlock, Easterhouse and Barlanark in the northeast, Drumchapel in the northwest, and Pollock and Castlemilk in the southwest. Estates like Castlemilk were vast and projected to have populations greater than Perth, but the problems that arose later were not so obvious then, and it is easy to be wise with hindsight. When the estates were built they were an answer to an immediate and pressing need, although not all the people re-housed in them were happy to leave the old, crumbling, but friendly and familiar slums. They arrived in the new schemes like homesteaders settling the Wild West and found themselves among the unfamiliar hills and sheep, with no cinemas, no pubs and only a handful of shops. Before long, the valleys around Glasgow were covered with a new generation of tenements.

The lorry rattled along Gartocher Road, and with a metal-shearing whine set off up Hallhill Road past Sandymount Cemetery.

'Are you sure your dad's all right in the back, Jim?' asked Mrs. Ritchie, raising her voice over the noise of the engine.

Jim gritted his teeth and tried to get the reluctant gear-stick down into third. 'Aye,' he said. 'Of course he is, mammy!' With a sound like a dog caught in a mangle the ancient gear-box responded. 'The wean's bed is tied across the back,' he went on, forestalling her next comment, 'and I wedged the armchair in next to your wardrobe, so he'll be all right. Don't you worry. He'll still be there when we get to Barlanark.'

Mrs. Ritchie shook her head. 'I'm too old for all this flitting,' she moaned. 'What wis wrong with Cumberland Street? That's what I want to know.'

Jim stared aggressively at the white line down the middle of the road. 'Och, come on, mammy,' he replied impatiently. 'You know fine what was wrong with the old place. It was damp, for a start. There were holes in the roof, wan lavvy between four families, rats, the stairs were crumblin'!' He stopped himself, knowing that the list could go on for a long time.

'But it was hame,' his mother said sadly. 'I won't know the neighbours out here in the country. Look at that, son. All fields. There's a cemetery. That's where I'll be going soon, likely.'

'Don't talk daft, mammy.' He looked at her, then swerved violently as he saw a cat crossing in front of the lorry.

'You should keep your eyes on the road, son,' his mother said. 'Don't let me distract you. That's all I am, a distraction.'

Jim bit his lip. 'The country air out here in Barlanark will do you good, mammy,' he replied, letting his breath out slowly. 'Cows an' sheep an' that. The weans can get to play in the fields.'

'But will I still be able to get down to the corner shop?' she asked pitifully.

'Och, I'm sure you will, mammy.' Jim changed up to fourth gear again. The warning light for the oil flickered, but it always did, so he ignored it.

His mother continued to ramble on as he turned left into Kentallen Road. '. . . and now you're merrit with weans and a good wee wife,' Mrs. Ritchie went on. 'And here we are, over the hills and far away, going to Bar ... something or other.'

'Barlanark, mammy. I've told you it's Barlanark,' he replied in exasperation. 'This is us. Kentallen Road, and there's Mima at the windy.'

'Is yer daddy all right at the back?' his mother asked.

He pulled into the kerb and braked hard. 'Mammy,' he said, 'you've been askin' me about daddy all the way across Glasgow. We've stopped now. There you are. Have a look for yourself.'

Tucking her hair under her headscarf she glanced through the window in the back of the cab. 'Oh aye! That's your daddy all over. Fast asleep.'

'Not for long,' said Jim, opening the door of the cab and jumping down. 'Da!' he called out. 'Daddy, wake up! C'mon and give us a hand!'

His father yawned and stretched. 'Is this it, Jim?' he said. 'They've got an awful big sky out here!'

The rising whistle of a kettle came from the kitchen as old Mr. Ritchie stared out of the window of the freshly-painted room. 'I can grow my plants out on that balcony, ye know,' he said with his back to the family. 'It won't be the same as the allotment, mind ye, but I suppose I'll manage.'

Jim's wife Mima bustled in from the kitchen. 'I don't know about that, granda,' she said, putting the teapot down on the table. 'I don't think the Corporation will let you.'

Old Mr. Ritchie turned away from the window. 'There's some view out there,' he said, nodding. 'You can see to the big stack at the back of Queen Street. Some view.'

The door opened again and the sound of running water came from down the hall.

'You'll need to keep that toilet nice, Mima,' Mrs. Ritchie interrupted, turning towards her daughter-in-law. 'It's just lovely.'

'Aye, mammy,' Mima replied. 'But it's ours. Nobody else'll be using it. Just this family.'

'I know that, dearie,' the old lady shook her head. 'But

what if the neighbours come in? I haven't seen the neighbours yet.'

'Give's a chance, mammy,' Jim said. 'We're just in.'

'Where are the weans?' his mother demanded.

'Away out to play, mammy,' said Mima hastily before Jim had a chance to say anything.

'Well they'll need tae watch they don't get bitten by nothing,' Mrs. Ritchie remarked sagely. 'It's no' safe here like it was at Gorbals Cross. Ye did tell them to watch out for wild beasties, didn't ye Mima?'

'Yes, mammy,' Mima replied without looking up. 'That's your tea out.'

'We should have something a bit stronger,' grinned old Mr. Ritchie. 'D'ye fancy going along the road later, Jim?'

Jim looked up at his father doubtfully. 'I've been meaning to tell you, da,' he said in a quiet voice.

'Tell me whit?' his father replied.

'Well, ye see,' Jim began. 'There's no pubs in Barlanark. The nearest is about two or three miles away.'

Silence descended like a velvet cloth on a feather bed.

'Did you say . . . nae pubs?' his father asked in disbelief. 'Och, you must be joking. You are, aren't you, son?'

'Er, no, da,' said Jim seriously. 'Your tea's gettin' cold.'

'In the name of fortune!' his father replied angrily. 'You mean if I want a drink, I'm going to have to go for a hike, is that it?'

'Not at all,' Jim said soothingly. 'There's a bus to Shettleston Road every half hour. We can go out later if you want.'

His father stamped off and stood, looking out of the window in silence. 'Great that is,' he muttered after a minute or two.

As they sat drinking their tea the quiet became almost audible. All their lives they had lived and slept with the noise of the city, the roar of traffic and the clamour of the yards. The family sat together in the bright new room, old Mr. Ritchie still with his back to them. In that awful silence, the clinking of the cups sounded like the tolling of a bell.

Like a stone breaking the ice, the living-room door flew open with a crash.

Wee Net ran into the room, tears streaming down her cheeks. 'Oh mammydaddy, mammydaddy, mammydaddy,' she bawled.

'What is it, Net, ma wee pet?' said Mima, sweeping her up into her arms. 'Tell your mammy all about it.'

'Oh mammydaddy,' yelled wee Net, girning wetly on her mother's shoulder. 'The big dug came and Sandy said . . . and then the man said, "Get oot!" and the sheep ran awa', and dugs have puppies, no' kittens like rabbits, and . . . and . . . He waved his big stick and said he's get the polis, and we should go back where we came from, and . . . and . . .' she dissolved into uncontrollable sobs and sniffles.

'What are you talking about?' said Jim, leaping to his feet. 'Where's your brother? What happened?'

'Leave her alone,' Mima whispered. 'Can't you see she's upset? Now. Tell your mammy, ma wee lamb pet.'

Wee Net looked round the room. Her nose was running and her eyes were big with fright. 'We were just playing with the nice sheepsies,' she began. 'Then a big dug came along and barked, and a farmer man said we should go hame, and Sandy's hidin'.' She started to sob. 'Can we, mammy, eh no?' she wailed. 'Me want to go hame.'

'Shh . . . darlin'. Shh, now,' Mima cuddled her.

'This is our hame, Net,' Jim said. 'We live here now.'

Net looked up at her father and rubbed her eyes with her fingers. 'Well, me no' like it, da,' she said. 'There's no' even a proper wash-hoose down the back for playin' stot-aff-the-wall or hideys or nothin' . . .'

Old Mr. Ritchie was still staring out of the window. 'Here's Sandy coming,' he said without turning round. 'Any of youse fancy lamb for your dinner?'

THE WEE ELVES IN THE BASEMENT

It was 1977 and it was Christmas. A man who dropped his car keys down a drain got his head and shoulders jammed when he tried to get them back again. According to the average wage tables for Scotland, it took 3 hours and 29 minutes to earn the cost of a bottle of whisky. Scotland was on its way to Argentina, and as the rain and sleet and frost paid their seasonal visits to the pedestrian precincts of Glasgow, showering the potted shrubs in Sauchiehall Street and Buchanan Street and filling the great hole where the magic new underground was going to be, Christmas loomed ever closer. Cutbacks had hit the Christmas lights in George Square, but it was still worth filling the car with the family and sitting in traffic jams along St. Vincent Street or Union Street. Christmas in Glasgow had been getting steadily more 'English', or at least 'Dickensian', over the years and turkeys and plum-pudding, together with the odd carry-out or two, came second only to toys. In every big store there was a certain magic grotto that the weans of Clydeside were desperate to visit, for when Christmas comes, it brings wee elves to the basements of large department stores and a certain old man in a white beard just waiting to ask the big question 'And what do you want from Santa?'

The Salvation Army was blasting out 'Rudolph the Red-Nosed Reindeer' as the strings of coloured light bulbs swung backwards and forwards above the heads of the hurrying shoppers in the Buchanan Street pedestrian precinct. The shop windows were full of wonders and tinsel, and in front of the bank a small figure in tartan trews was playing the violin behind his back.

Mrs. McKendrick, parcels up to her nose, bustled round

the corner of Gordon Street. 'Keep up, Tommy!' she called to the little boy trailing behind her. 'How can I carry all this and keep going back for you?'

'But mammy,' Tommy said. 'There's a clown with ears that light up in the windy over there.'

'So there is, darlin',' she replied, hurrying on. 'That's lovely. Hurry up!'

Tommy whined and hung onto the folds of her maxi. 'But you didn't look,' he girned. 'Look! There he is!'

'I saw it,' she said, sitting down heavily on one of the benches. 'Mammy needs a rest. Be a good boy now.'

The woman beside her smiled sympathetically. 'I know what it's like,' she shook her head.

Tommy's mother put her parcels down carefully. 'Every year I promise myself I'll not leave things to the last minute, and every year it's the same story.'

'Och, I'm the same,' her companion agreed. 'I've been on my feet all day, and the shops are just mobbed. I don't know where the money's coming from.'

Mrs. McKendrick looked at the fur-collared coat the woman was wearing. The scent of a Van Cleef perfume wafted over her. 'Well they are spending it like it's going out of style,' she replied a little stiffly. 'Tommy!' she called out. 'Don't wander off! Come here or you'll get it when we get hame. See if it wisny Christmas, my lad. But you do it for them don't you?' she asked, turning to the stranger.

The lady smiled. 'That's right,' she said. 'If it wasn't for them, I don't think I'd bother.'

Mrs. McKendrick turned round to see where Tommy had gone.

She saw, to her horror, that he was halfway up the free-standing sculpture in the middle of the pedestrian precinct. 'Tommy!' she shouted. 'Tommy! Just you get down offa there! Here's the man comin'. Get down when I tell you!'

'I can't,' came the wavering reply. 'I'm stuck!'

'You get down when I tell you to,' his mother cried, panicking, 'Santa disny come to boys that climb up on whatever it is you've climbed up on.'

'I think it's meant to be a tramcar or a bird or something,' the woman said helpfully.

'Well, it's no' meant to be climbed on anyway,' Mrs. McKendrick replied tartly. 'Tommy! Get down here!'

'Mammy!' he wailed. 'Mammy!' and toppled off the object like a sparrow with vertigo.

Mrs. McKendrick rushed across to him and sat him up, brushing the sleeves of his coat with her hand. 'Your good new overcoat,' she said anxiously. 'Tommy! Speak to me!'

He opened his eyes and looked at her. 'What do you want me to say, mammy?' he asked.

She dragged him to his feet unceremoniously. 'You . . . you wee tyke,' she raged. 'For two pins I'd clap your lug, so I would. There's not a thing wrong with you. And look at those good shoes! They don't grow on trees. They're all scuffed. Oh you bad, bad boy.' She took him by the scruff of the neck and shook him till his gloves fell off.

'But . . . but mammy,' he whined. 'I just wanted a better look at the tree.'

'What tree?' she asked angrily.

'That big Christmas tree down there outside the big shop,' he said hopefully as she let go of him. 'Kin we go and see that, mammy? Kin we? Eh no?'

The stranger had walked over to see if Tommy was all right. 'It is Christmas,' she smiled. 'The Christmas spirit, you know.'

Mrs. McKendrick gave her a venomous glance. 'Aye, well, we'll see. Come on you,' she said grabbing her parcels and bundling Tommy off in front of her. 'One more peep out of you and you'll no live till Christmas,' she threatened. 'And if you think I'm taking you up to see Santa in that store after the way you've behaved, you've got another think coming.'

The toy department had never been so busy. Counters and stands were piled high with every description of toy, gadget, game and kit. Robots buzzed, tanks sparked, and the miniature midnight express rushed through sleeping plastic villages. Christmas carols boomed out across the crowded floor and enormous cut-out sleighs and snowmen spun lazily in the warm air rising from the clockwork wonderland.

Mrs. McKendrick dragged her son through the crowds. 'Why you couldn't be satisfied with the first shop we went into, I don't know,' she said, elbowing her way along.

'But that wasn't the real Santa!' Tommy replied. 'He had glasses.'

'Well this is the real Santa in here,' she assured him.

'How do you know, mammy?' Tommy asked.

'Because I'm telling you it is,' she answered, tightening her grip on his hand.

'This way to Santa's grotto, this way to Santa's Grotto,' the assistant in the gnome's costume said, taking Tommy's ticket. 'In you go now, son.'

Tommy walked under the arch into the sparkling dimness of the cave. The faint sound of hammering greeted him, a regular tap, tap . . . tom, tap. Dwarves were singing 'Hi Ho, Hi Ho' somewhere beyond the picture of a giant's castle and at the back of the cave on a glittering chair there sat an old man with a long, long snowy beard.

'And who do we have here?' the old man said in a deep, booming voice.

'M . . . me,' Tommy replied, walking towards him and looking up.

Dark eyes twinkled with amusement as they looked down at him. 'And who is "me"?' asked the man.

'Tommy McKendrick,' Tommy said in a small voice.

'Well, Tommy,' said the man, lifting him up onto his knee. 'Have you been a good boy?'

'Aye, mister,' said Tommy.

'Don't you know who I am?' the man asked. He smiled, and his eyes almost vanished under huge bushy white eyebrows.

'I . . . I think so,' said Tommy uncertainly. 'You're Santa.'

'You think so!' said the man. 'Of course I am.'

'There canna be two of you, can there?' Tommy asked doubtfully.

'Well,' the man said seriously. 'I do have a lot of helpers

you know, but there's only one real Santa.'

'And you're him?' Tommy persisted.

'Yes!' Santa boomed. 'Can't you hear my elves making toys?'

'They've left it a bit late,' Tommy said.

'It's never too late to start getting ready for next year,' Santa countered.

'Kin I ask you a question?' the wee boy said.

'Of course you can,' Santa smiled. 'Please do, Tommy.'

'Do you wear glasses?' asked Tommy.

'Why no, it's far too frosty at the North Pole,' Santa chuckled. 'You see, they would always be icing up!'

'Well that's all right then,' Tommy replied with relief. 'But yer helper down the road disna know that. You should crack down on them, Santa. They'll gie ye a bad name.'

'I'll do that, Tommy,' Santa said quietly.

Suddenly the wee boy took hold of Santa's wrist. 'Here!' he exclaimed suspiciously. 'You've got a watch on!'

'Ahh. But I need that,' said Santa. 'The nights at the North Pole, as every schoolboy knows, are six months long. How would I know when it's time to get up and come to Glasgow for Christmas?'

'Aww . . . that's all right then,' said Tommy with relief. 'Ye had me worried there for a minute, Santa. Now. I'd like a big train, a supersonic whizz-bang bomber, a space-warp time-capsule and a tin of that green stuff that runs down the door knob.'

'Where have you been?' asked his mother anxiously when he emerged from the grotto.

'Talking to Santa,' Tommy replied.

'Don't make things up now,' she said. 'The man's just told me you should have waited outside. 'Santa's been away for his tea break. There he is comin' now, with the glasses.'

COBBLESTONES AND COMPUTERS

From 1780 to the 1980s Glasgow has weathered many storms and seen its skyline change from low tile roofs pointing crazily at the sky into steeples and green copper domes, and then move on into the twentieth century and the skyscraper age. As a custodian of the Word, the city has had its printers and its publishers, its booksellers, libraries and newspapers, but when John Mennons the printer put the first edition of the *Glasgow Advertiser* 'to bed' in 1783, he began a story that is still being told today. When he printed the news that Britain had formally recognized the independence of the United States, he little imagined that the *Glasgow Advertiser*, re-named the *Glasgow Herald*, would still be 'holding the presses' two hundred years later in a world of flight and fusion, oil and computers, in a city without carriages or powdered wigs or cobblestones.

From the *Advertiser*'s early days at the Tontine Close in the Trongate, where Mennons' agent brought the news gathered at the Tontine Coffee Rooms, to the move via Bell Street in the Candleriggs to the Rennie Mackintosh building in Mitchell Street, and finally to Albion Street in July 1980, Mennons' creation has brought events at home and abroad to Glasgow for the better part of 60,000 mornings. The story of the paper, the story of the transmutation of metal type, little different from the kind used by Gutenberg and Caxton, into floppy discs and video display units by the alchemy of modern technology, is, in a sense, the story of the city itself.

The printing press stood at the back of the long, low room. John Mennons wiped his fingers on his leather apron, leaned forward, and brought the heavy lever down. The machinery clanked, locked, then unlocked as he lifted it again. Making sure the platen was well clear, he lifted the sheet of paper from the type-frame carefully and held it up. 'Here you are, William,' he said, handing it to his apprentice.

'Just add it to the pile, sir?' the boy asked.

'Not at all, you daftie,' his master replied crossly. 'It's not dry yet. Hang it up with the others. Make haste now! We have the whole edition to print!' He ran the roller across the velvety surface of the ink-plate and then over the type. The letters stood out, strong and black. He took a blank sheet and laid it on the type, bringing the platen down again. The press clanked and shook as another copy of the *Glasgow Advertiser* was printed.

The elderly gentleman, cheeks rouged and wig powdered, coughed artificially as John Mennons squared up the completed pile of newspapers.

'Here you are, Robin,' Mennons said, handing him a copy of the paper without looking up.

Robin McNair, Mennons' wife's grandfather, was a grocer of some substance and eccentricity, with an opinion on anything and everything. 'That looks fine again, John,' he commented, putting on a pair of rectangular spectacles held together by a small strip of wood and squinting at the columns. 'Anything on my carriage?'

'Well, to tell the truth, the *Advertiser*'s business is all the news,' John Mennons replied, 'but I must confess, your item was a little, er . . . late in for this edition.'

Robin McNair waved the paper at him and glared. 'Aye, aye, but yon tax is news in the first degree, John,' he said, raising his eyebrows till they looked as if they were going to fall off the side of his forehead. 'A tax on two-wheeled carriages is a direct threat to all our liberties, man! I'm telling you, John, there are others who would do as I did and fit runners to their coaches to take their families to church. It's called a protest, man! That's news! You could tell from the crowds as we slid along over the cobbles that they thought it at least a novel notion.'

'Oh, there's no denying it's that,' replied Mennons, looking away. 'But I've no time for such gestures myself.

I'm a burgess with a paper to print.'

'I know you are, John,' the sprightly old man nodded. 'And I like ye for't, but keep in mind now, I may be your dear Jeannie's grandpa, but I'm more than that, much more. You have a grocer and a friend in me.'

'Oh yes, Robin, that's fine. Most good of ye,' said John Mennons, humouring him.

'That's them all checked over now, Mr. Mennons,' called William from behind the pile of newspapers.

'I can see that you are busy the now, John,' said the visitor. 'I'll away. If you are down by later on at the Tontine, I'll share a pipe with you. Now mind what I said about runners and wheels!' He opened the door and made his way down the stairs to the close.

'Oh aye, Robin,' John Mennons smiled to himself, walking across to the precious pile of newspapers. 'Wheels right enough. Wheels within wheels.'

'What was that, sir?' William asked, puzzled.

'Nothing at all, laddie,' said John Mennons, shaking his head. 'I'm getting as bad as he is. Is that you done?'

'Aye, Mr. Mennons,' William replied with alacrity. 'All ready to take down to the plainstanes.'

'I'll not be coming down today,' his master said, 'so you take my bundle and give it to the boy down the stair. Now you've not to push the *Advertiser* into people's hands as if it was some kind of ultimatum. The *Advertiser* can advertise itself just by being there. Off you go now.'

'Yes,' replied the boy, hurrying down the stairs. 'Here's Mr. Mathie comin' up,' he called back.

Benjamin Mathie, who claimed John Knox as an ancestor, walked towards John Mennons, grinning expansively. 'The world's coming and going up the Tontine Close today,' he said, shaking John's hand vigorously. 'I saw "Tom Paine" going down the stairs.'

'Robin McNair?' John Mennons chuckled. 'And what can the office of the *Glasgow Advertiser* do for you?'

'Och, I'd no business until later and the Trades House isn't going to go away, so . . .' He leaned his black malacca cane against the bench with painstaking nicety. 'So I thought it an ideal moment to discuss a small venture I have in mind.'

'Touching on our partnership?' the printer asked.

'No, no, that's not it,' Mathie shook his head.

'You intrigue me, Benjamin,' John Mennons replied. 'Now, let's think what this "matter" can be. Apart from clerkship to the Trades House, and clerkship to Rutherglen, and clerkship to the Highland Society, the law, and your local history, you've not left much for a body to speculate on. There must be something!'

'Actually it's yourself,' Mathie went on. 'You're overdoing it, John. It's common knowledge that you spend your nights in here reading despatches and mails, editing and heaven knows what else. You've got help now, and the new type. If the paper is going to come out twice a week and you take on my directories, the lottery tickets and all the rest, other hands than yours will have to do the work. You'll kill yourself, man!'

'Did Jean set you up to this?' John Mennons asked.

'Not at all,' his friend replied hotly, 'but, Lord, man! You still sell the thing yourself!'

'It's not a "thing",' John Mennons said, hurt. 'It's my work, and I like it.'

'Well, so long as you realize it's not overfond of you,' Mathie answered with a shake of his head. 'But there's no denying you are a man o' pairts, and that's what's going to turn Glasgow into a great city, people with more than one string to their bow.'

'You are a terrible man for the preaching,' laughed John Mennons, clapping his friend on the shoulder. 'But if you want to discuss the new printing work, there's no more private place than a booth off the smoke-room at the Tontine.'

'Your wife's grandfather went down there, did he not?' asked Mathie, picking up his cane.

'Oh we'll be all right I should think, Benjamin,' Mennons laughed. 'So long as we change our wheels for runners before we go in.'

His friend laughed. 'I was hearing about that,' he said.

'The man's a right character.'

'Well, I'd rather not be the "advertiser" of that,' John winked. 'He is a relative, you know.'

'If you ask me, it runs in the family,' said Benjamin Mathie, pretending not to see the face John Mennons made as they walked down the stairs towards the cobblestones of the Trongate.

The characters on the video display unit changed in rapid succession as the keyboard operator ran through the programme. As the machine spoke to the man in coloured lights the Assistant Editor looked round the huge room. Rows of machines stood winking and flickering, the scene more like something out of Mission Control at Houston than the offices of a newspaper. Outside, a jet fighter on the back of an enormous lorry rumbled past the Trongate on it's way to a display in George Square, and the telex in the next room chattered out messages from Java and New Jersey.

'That was quite a flitting,' the man said.

'Changed days,' the Editor nodded. 'In a way we're back where everything started. The old Greyfriars Monastery was just round the corner from here over eight hundred years ago. To think somebody sat around near here hardening their quill pen in hot sand before getting started on a little bit of illumination!'

'More flexible deadlines in those days,' the Assitant Editor laughed. 'I think we have just as much "illuminating" to do as they had.'

'Well, it's early days,' the Editor replied, looking out of the window as the tail fin of the Hawker Harrier passed the Old College Bar. 'The first two hundred years are the hardest.'

SHIPYARD IN THE SKY

The 2080s promised to be a happy time. The planet derived unlimited power from a vast world-girdling system of satellite mirror-stations that sent the energy of the sun direct to Earth, carried on the fiery bridge of the particle beam. To an observer in space, the power spokes radiated from the equator like a catherine wheel, and the mirrors, each twenty miles in diameter and two molecules thick, floated above the earth with serene brilliance. The laws that followed the Ten-Minute War, outlawing the experiments in biological engineering that had threatened to produce a new and terrifying man, had at last removed the old tensions and mistrust between nations. The countries of the earth seemed to have begun to outlive their adolescence and were sharing what they had without rancour and trying to realize the power of the new technology for good. The re-forming of the planets Mars and Venus was well in hand and the project to dismantle the planet Jupiter was beyond the planning stage. In Glasgow, one of the designated 'rural areas' of the West European Consortium, shipping was about to become a major industry for the first time in over a hundred and twenty years.

Jo McCulloch glanced out of the window of the rapid transit capsule. The forested area around the Scottish Exhibition Centre, one of the grand old buildings of the region, sparkled in the sunlight after the six o'clock rain. It always rained at six o'clock, but in Scotland Sundays were kept rain-free, and during the forest tourist season and on Christmas Day the Weather Control Centre chilled the clouds sufficiently to produce snow.

The glassite container slowed, assumed a different polarity, and he walked through the wall as if it had been smoke.

He had arranged to meet Harry Watt at the Clydebank Memorial Oil Rig, but with the 'rural season' open and the Clyde packed with pleasure craft, he had punched up his friend's personal co-ordinates and changed the meeting place to the picturesque tower blocks and warehouses of old twentieth-century Anderston.

Harry sat deep in thought, the tall glass of iced lemon untouched in front of him. The sight of teenage tobacco-smokers illegally puffing away at the outlawed weed in defiance of law and custom had shocked him, and the timely arrival of the Public Control Department had done nothing to dispel the feeling of unease that had been growing on him all day.

Jo's call had caught him in the middle of a design parameter, and although his work for Trans-Global Engineering seldom took him away from his house unit or his beloved steam-engine collection, he realized that only the companionship of another human being would assure him that his ideas were not altogether wild and impossible. He looked at the plastic plants around him with disgust. The Conservation Directorate, the body that had replaced the old United Nations, had exercised a harsh control over the private ownership of greenery of any sort, but that had been years ago, in the early 2020s, and these pathetic polythene rubber plants were a hangover from an earlier, more dismal age before people had realized that technology could provide almost anything in unlimited quantities by simply re-arranging the molecules. Almost anything, except what he had in mind.

Jo McCulloch walked into the café-bar and waved to his friend. 'Well?' he asked, sitting down. 'What kind of a welcome is that?'

'Sorry,' Harry said, forcing a grin. 'I've got a wee idea that I want to try out on you.'

'Sounds ominous,' Jo replied, dialling hims

'This is just between ourselves,' Harry said
button and the familiar privacy of a beam
around them. 'That's better,' he continu

little. 'I want to talk to you about ships.'

Jo favoured his friend with a long cool glance. In a world where work and leisure, education and enjoyment were inextricably mixed, men and women could have hobbies that ranged from playing chess with dolphins to cultivating musical begonias, but Harry was an intelligent man and essentially practical.

'You know they used to build ships near here,' he said suddenly.

'I've done my Grade Modules,' Jo replied. 'The Clyde used to be famous for its ships a century or so ago.'

'Well, think back to those Grade Modules you did as a kid,' Harry continued earnestly. 'Remember how the Clyde Valley became the European centre for micro-electronics in the late 80s and early 90s?'

'Tell me something I don't know,' said Jo, dialling a passion fruit impatiently. The de-integrator accepted the pips obligingly with a silent flash of light.

'Well, you know I've been involved in the Jupiter Project,' Harry said, leaning forward.

'Really?' Jo replied, not committing himself.

'Well I have. Take my word for it,' Harry continued. 'That's going to occupy the combined world tech for the next eighty years, and for what?' He thumped the shiny black table with his fist.

A wafer-screen popped out of the surface beside his hand. 'Did you want something, sir?' asked a pleasant female voice.

'No, dammit!' Harry shouted. 'And you're in a spy-field. Beat it!'

'Sorry, pardon me,' said the computer, offended. The screen vanished into the featureless table.

'This whole project to build a new series of planetoids is stupid and old-fashioned,' Harry continued. 'It's like that bridge that collapsed last year.'

'The Forth Bridge,' Jo said quietly.

'Yes, that one,' Harry went on. 'Oh, it was marvellous in its day, but the day of the dinosaurs is over. We don't need make twenty new worlds. We can have thousands, millions.' He stared at his friend, wild-eyed.

'Where?' asked Jo, puzzled.

'What d'you mean "where"?' Harry replied. 'Up there!' He pointed at the ceiling.

Jo looked at him with dawning realization. 'You mean the stars, don't you?' he asked.

Harry nodded.

'Harry,' Joe said after a moment's pause. 'When you and I did Middle-Modular Physics at Strathclyde did somebody never mention a wee thing called the "universal constant", the speed of light?'

'Oh that,' said Harry with a wave of his hand. 'What about Professor MacLean?'

'But ... but that was only a theory, sheer speculation.'

'Was it?' Harry sneered. 'It was, but it isn't now. Not since yesterday.' He reached beneath the table and produced an old-fashioned canvas bag, made from natural fibre. He lifted it up and thumped it on the table. The Desireomat started to rise out of the table again, but he thumped it down angrily. 'Look at this!' he said, his hands shaking with excitement as he lifted a small, heavy object out of the satchel. It was about the size of an egg, but flattened at either end, blueish in colour and supported by five spindly pins or bolts. Somewhere deep inside it a captive glow pulsed intermittently. 'That,' he announced after a dramatic pause, 'is it!'

'But what is it?' Joe asked, reaching out to pick it up.

'Don't touch it,' Harry moved the object deftly out of Jo's reach. 'It's delicate. This is a thousand worlds, or rather, the means of getting there. I've solved the MacLean-Svenson equations, Joe. It was quite easy really after I linked into Mind Central on Pantelleria.'

'You did *what*?' Jo gasped. The central world-computer on the small rocky island off the southern tip of Italy was off limits to any individual. Its power and the risks of contacting it were too great. That Harry could penetrate the security codes was itself little short of a miracle.

'It said it had been waiting for me,' Harry said blandly. 'The night I got through the four-vid went wild, the view-wall collapsed, and there was just this . . . this voice in my mind. It said: "You have been forecast." Just like that. Then it showed me where I had been going wrong. All those months I had been working in total darkness and I hadn't realized. Anyway, this is the drive everyone's been searching for for fifty years. It's not an engine really, it's a direction-changer. It will take a flight path, whatever the speed, and turn it inside out four ways at once. It abolishes distance. All travel will become instantaneous!'

Without warning the spy-screen collapsed and the table was surrounded by a ring of black-visored Public Control Engineers. 'Do not move,' said a pleasant voice. 'All resistance is counter to public order!'

Suddenly the speaker was elbowed aside by a man dressed in plain battle-gold.

'That's mine!' gasped Harry as his precious device vanished inside a respectable plastic bag.

'It will be kept until suitable enquiries have been made,' said the golden officer coldly.

'But the Central Computer itself helped me!' Harry protested. 'Don't you understand? This is the means to reach the stars!'

'Central may have neglected to mention it,' replied the officer, 'but as of last night, the stars have reached us.'

Altair, Sirius and the blue-white blaze of Vega shone down on the ancient Market Cross of Glasgow. The Town House, lovingly restored, leaned comfortably against the square pinnacle of the Tolbooth. To the starship that had crossed a million years of space, markets and sailing ships, dance halls, trams and bombers were less than an instant, and while the world waited to see what news the silent visitor from the dark would bring, a man called Watt, set free without his engine, walked beside the Clyde on the night Earth's childhood ended.